Wild Cats

Other books by C. B. COLBY

WHO WENT THERE?

WHO LIVES THERE?

COLBY'S NATURE ADVENTURES

FISH & WILDLIFE

SOIL SAVERS

TALL TIMBER

AMERICA'S NATURAL WONDERS

PARK RANGER

BETTER HOMES & GARDENS FAMILY CAMPING

SNOW SURVEYORS

FIRST FISH

FIRST RIFLE

FIRST CAMPING TRIP

FIRST BOW AND ARROW

FIRST BOAT

FIRST HUNT

FUR AND FURY: The Talented Weasel Family (*Mustelidae*)

Edited by C. B. COLBY

PETS

Wild Cats

by C. B. COLBY

DUELL, SLOAN AND PEARCE
New York

First edition

Affiliate of
MEREDITH PRESS
Des Moines & New York

Library of Congress Catalogue Card Number: 64-13793

MANUFACTURED IN THE UNITED STATES OF AMERICA FOR MEREDITH PRESS

VAN REES PRESS • NEW YORK

CONTENTS

5

INTRODUCING THE CAT FAMILY

A long time ago, about fifty million years, give or take a few hundred centuries either way, the first cats began to hunt for game through the Eocene forests and jungles. Being all carnivorous (flesh eaters), perhaps their first square meals even then consisted of Eocene-age mice. It is hard to say, for none of these earliest of the felines left any trace.

About twenty million years later, during the Oligocene period, the cats began to divide as a type of animal into two branches of the clan. One, including the outlandish saber-toothed tiger and some other huge cats, headed off in one direction and to eventual oblivion. The other branch, mostly composed of smaller felines, headed out across the young world and is still here today in assorted sizes, coats, and dispositions. Fortunately for us humans, this happened, for a world without cats would lack a lot of fun and excitement, and would probably be overly full of mice.

The saber-toothed tiger, as a fine example of what happened to the other branch of the cat clan, developed vast eight-inch upper canine teeth which were literally sabers, or at least daggers. With these the great cats used to stab their prey, so

7

that they bled to death. They stabbed mastodons, slow-moving giant sloths, and other animals of the period too slow to escape their attack. Eventually, through the ages, these slow-moving dinners all died off, leaving the saber-toothed cat with a huge problem on his paws. The remaining game was much too agile for him to stab, and so, as the great saber teeth prevented him from using his mouth for any other type of attack, he, too, eventually vanished, specialized by nature right out of existence. Only the fossils of the saber-toothed cats and their kind remain to tell the story.

The other branch of the Felidae family, less specialized in their weapons, found plenty to live upon and readily adapted to the changing ages. The branch of smaller cats spread out from Asia, where it is believed they first developed, into almost all parts of the world in one shape or another. Only four areas were catless: the two polar regions, New Zealand, and Australia.

Some natural-history historians believe that all cats were originally dressed in plain buff-colored coats, but that over the ages they developed patterned coats to serve as camouflage for themselves in the areas in which they lived and hunted. It is also suspected that even some of these have again changed back to plain coats for better camouflage on their hunting ranges in today's world.

For example, the plainly dressed mountain lion and the African lion, also plainly dressed when mature, all arrive in spots and stripes when they are born, perhaps as evolutionary throwbacks to ancient ancestors who were so marked even when fully grown.

It is true that animals today still adapt their coloring to where they live, even if of the same species. Bobcats living in the desert, as a case in point, are lighter, more sandy in color, and wear fewer spots than their northern relatives who do their hunting in dark timberlands. Jaguars, pretty sporty gents no matter where they live, are even more splashily dressed when you find them in the sunlight-spattered jungles of South America, where everything is bright light and shadow. Members of the leopard family—noted for their yellow coats and black spots—who live in the snow and ice countries have changed their outfits for coats of soft grays and whites, more nearly to match the backgrounds where they must hunt and kill to survive. And so it goes.

All members of the Felidae family have several characteristics in common, as do all members of other of nature's families. The cats (with one exception, the cheetah) all have retractile claws which can either be concealed in the tops of their toes for silent walking and keeping the points sharp, or shot out of their cases as unbelievably effective weapons. They all dig holes in which to deposit their droppings, which they fill after use—an instinctive habit to conceal the fact that they are hunting in the area. They all use scratching trees or posts upon which to sharpen their claws, and they almost without exception purr when contented, a voice trick exclusive with cats, whether a mountain lion in its rocky lair or the tabby on your hearth. They have all developed long, stiff whiskers equipped with sensitive nerves at the base so that they can be used to feel their way through openings or past obstructions in the dark, and their eyes are specialized for night vision far beyond those of man and many other creatures.

The pupils of a cat's eyes are closed into small slits during the day, almost like the primitive sunglasses used by Eskimos, a flat slab of bone or wood with tiny horizontal slits cut through the material. At night, however, the cat's pupil-slits open up until the whole eye seems almost a giant pupil, so that any available light can be gathered in to make getting about easier. Cats cannot see in total darkness any more than can any other creature, but their eyes do collect far more light at night. Thus it is possible for them to get around quite easily when others less fortunate can hardly see a thing or not at all.

Usually cats as individuals can and will live alone and like it, and with apparent indifference to whether or not you are around to care for their needs. Even domestic cats are pretty independent and will get along without too much attention, provided they can hunt for themselves. Tame domestic cats and pampered pets, lost or abandoned, will easily and quickly revert to the wild state. They will go right on living, almost as though nothing had happened, quickly learning to catch wild food and soon becoming as wild and difficult to capture as any of their normally wild relatives on the following pages. Such feral cats which have returned to the wild state are perhaps the worst possible enemy of small wildlife in the area. They are particularly prone to kill songbirds, chipmunks, and rabbits.

Cats are not only rugged individuals but mighty intelligent ones as well, and are about the most efficient hunting machines ever produced by nature. Some species of cats have dreamed up hunting tricks that would make a Daniel Boone hide his head in shame. The ocelots, for instance, have learned to play "dead" to catch monkeys, one of their prime entrees. An ocelot will drape himself along a stout tree branch, with his tail hanging limply below, and remain motionless without a twitch when monkeys are in the neighborhood. Soon, one of the monkeys will spot the "dead" animal and set up a great hue and cry for all to come and see. Eventually one of the critters, elated over the death of his enemy, will get near enough to touch its fur, tweak an ear, or perhaps grab its tail—and that's the end of the little act for both of them.

Lions will plan an attack on an intended meal with all the skill of TV-Apaches planning an ambush on early settlers and their wagon train. Some will hide ahead, while others will drive the unsuspecting "settlers" straight for the ambush and tragedy.

Jaguars are reported to catch fish very neatly by lying on a low branch over a quiet pool and drooling into the water just below them. As the droplets splash into the still water, fish come up to investigate, and the cat splashes them out onto the bank with a swipe of his hooked paw.

Jaguars and tigers, by the way, are about the only wild cats which really enjoy going into the water, although all cats can swim well if need be. In spite of this dislike for bathing, all cats delight in washing themselves with their tongues. These unusual members are covered with small barbs facing back towards their throats and in the larger cats are so rough they can strip the flesh from bones as easily as you would with a rasp. These same little barbs serve as teeth with which to groom their sleek fur. Sometimes they are pretty hefty in their grooming, and I've seen a lioness literally "comb" her cub right off its feet in her enthusiasm to make him presentable. This seems to impress the youngster, for he soon begins to waggle his own small tongue over his hide in imitation of his fastidious elders.

Family life among the Felidae is usually a pretty pleasant and heart-warming thing to observe. The mother takes good care of her young, being most gentle in caring for them and permitting them to clamber over her, pounce on her twitching tail tip and generally act like kids of any kind. Parents often team up to carefully teach the offspring how to hunt and learn the business of getting ready to fend for themselves. They can also be stern parents as well, batting a youngster back into line if he appears to be getting too independent before his time. Sometimes you'll see a dignified lion father, tormented by a youngster, give him a sort of half-hearted slap with a "Get away boy, y' bother me!" expression; or he will get up and move away to a place where things are quieter. Often parents show real affection for each other by bringing their mates a choice piece of food, by licking and caressing one another, or by defending to the death an injured partner unable to flee.

The cats are generally nocturnal animals, doing most of their hunting at night, when their eyes give them a great advantage; but here again, as with other animal families, there are always those rugged characters who hunt when they darn well please, rules or no rules. Here, too, you will find individuals who just never conform to what the generally accepted picture of such a feline should be and act like. If you should encounter one of these off-beat cats, just assume he is the exception which goes to prove the rest of the clan DOES follow the rules.

In making my selections for this book I have tried to include all major wild cats which typify a species, or, if not representative of a species, have some unusual or especially interesting characteristics. There are many species so similar to others that only a scientist could know the difference, and so I have omitted them. There are, for example, several of the lynx clan which look alike and which have the same general silhouette, even to the ear tufts, of the Canada Lynx, so I have selected him, our northern neighbor, as pretty typical of all lynxes.

In the following chapters, you will find a wide variety of cats, dressed in plain coats, striped and spotted coats, some with dots, splotches and bars, and some with rosettes, bands, or all of them together. In real life they are even more flashy, for the colors range from buff to jet black (in the melanistic phase) and include orange, yellow, and various combinations of them all in one coat. The cats are a gaudy bunch, with a few exceptions made necessary by the drab backgrounds against which they must conceal themselves to survive. Whether you find a cat in the Canadian wilds or on the plains of Africa, you'll always find him interesting and well worth observing.

Some cats live high in the snow and ice country, some in steaming jungles, and some in hot, dry climates. However, being adaptable, they have simply adjusted their lives, appetites, and colorations to fit the surroundings. If there are trees, they have learned how to climb them with agility and skill for hunting; if there are none, they have simply forgotten how to climb them and do their hunting on the ground with greater skill, doing very well without possibly ever having climbed a tree. In snow country they grow thick fur coats with fur shoes to match, and they even grow larger feet, as in the case of the Canada lynx, for example, to make snow walking easier. Their "nine lives" are really three: intelligence, adaptability, and resourcefulness.

Cats are fascinating, whether curled up on your hearth, a kitten chasing a wind-blown leaf, or a mighty-muscled wild beast of prey stalking his dinner. All are basically the same under their wildly assorted skin colorings and could be the same animal with different dispositions to fit the sizes, for they all had a common ancestor back before history began.

In doing the research for this book, I met many new "wild" friends and not a few old ones, some behind bars and some behind trees. For my part, the meetings were most pleasant and even exciting, from the little Canada lynx kittens in beautiful Mont Tremblant Park in Canada to the elderly lioness who "played tag" with me behind her bars at the famed Bronx Zoo in New York. My thanks go to them, as well as to the others I met in between.

Besides the four-legged ladies and gentlemen and youngsters I observed and talked to, I met some mighty fine folks on two legs. Particularly warm thanks to Captain Maurice Coutu, CD, Director of Mont Tremblant Park, Province of Quebec, Canada, for his many courtesies and kindnesses, and for his making me a *surveillant auxiliaire* (auxiliary warden)—a unique honor indeed —of this wild and beautiful piece of "the country above," as they call it; and to his charming son Pierre, for letting me use his

13

picture in the book. Thanks also to my old friend J. Lear Grimmer, Associate Director of the famed National Park Zoo, Smithsonian Institution, in Washington, D.C., and to the personnel of the New York Zoological Society's great New York Zoological Park, better known as the Bronx Zoo, for putting up with my many questions and granting me many courtesies. Without the generous and enthusiastic help of such fine people, this book would not have been the exciting and pleasant project that it was.

Photograph by the author

A NOTE ON TRACKS

In collecting and preparing the paw- and track-print drawings for any book, an author-artist meets with not a few assorted technical problems, as I pointed out in my earlier book, *Fur and Fury*, which dealt with the weasel family.

Paw prints vary greatly with the surface upon which you find them, the particular animal which made them, and the weather conditions at the time they were made and also between the making and the finding of the tracks.

Even the activity of the print-maker can have a bearing on their clarity, and tracks from the same species can vary from animal to animal. After looking at the feet of a great many types and sizes of cats, measuring and examining bales of study skins and pelts at the American Museum of Natural History in New York, I can assure you that even the four feet of a single cat can show variances from paw to paw.

Members of the Felidae family all have five toes and claws on the front feet and four of each on the hind feet, to be sure, but, as in human hand- and footprints, there are still some variations to be found. Even experts argue hotly as to what is a typical leopard track, a jaguar track, or a mountain lion track.

On the following pages I have sketched "typical" tracks and paw prints of the various members of the cat family as I have found them to be. There are not as many variations in cat tracks as in weasel tracks, certainly, but I think you will find them interesting, especially as to size.

The next time you are in the woods, or lucky enough to explore a jungle or African plain where they might be found, keep an eye out for them near water holes, where the animals go to drink, or along game trails where they may stalk their dinners. If you have a cat, examine its feet and compare the size of the prints they make with some of those on the pages ahead. That alone will help you visualize the great and gorgeous cats which made the paw prints I have included.

Wild Cats

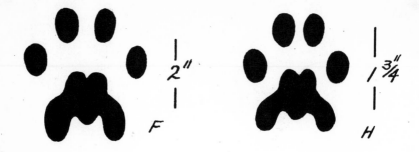

1. BOBCAT
Lynx rufus

One of the tales I used to relish as a young naturalist was told by an aunt of mine who spent the summers on a farm in State Line, New Hampshire, a tiny village near the Massachusetts line. One evening she had gone outside to bring in the pans of fresh milk cooling on the back porch. There, quite contentedly lapping the milk from one of the shallow pans, was what she thought was a whale of a big neighbor's cat. She flapped her apron at it and shooed it away in anger, only to have the "house cat" open its mouth, spit at her and let out a screech that almost soured the milk. It was a big bobcat lured from the nearby woods by the smell of fresh milk.

Almost anyone who has spent time in the woods from Nova Scotia to the West Coast or from Canada to Florida could have seen, heard, or spotted the tracks of this bobtailed wildcat. With the exception of some areas of the so-called corn-belt states, this animal roams over most of the original United States and

into Canada as well. It is also known as the wildcat, the bay lynx, and a few other names I am unable to repeat, especially those used when it lets out a screech right behind you in the night.

One fall, hunting in the Catskill Mountains of New York State, two other men and I drove to the end of a logging road to park the car. We had planned to sleep in the car, and got out to stretch before turning in. Apparently we had surprised a bob-cat with the headlights, and he had frozen where he was—almost beside us—as we stepped out of the vehicle. I remember I was just getting back into the car with one of the other chaps behind me when the cat let out one of his hair-raising screeches right in back of us.

To say we were startled would be the understatement of the season. To this day we have never been able to figure out how the fellow behind me was already inside the car trying to lock the doors when I got there myself. If you have never heard a healthy bobcat in good voice make a few comments in the dead of night, you have no idea of the effect it can have on the human nervous system. Thackeray described it as "a shriek and a yell like the devils of hell," and all I can say is that he, too, must have heard one himself.

Even when you know what kind of cat is making the noise, to hear one prowling around your tent at night, giving off a few low "yowls" from time to time, is not conducive to sound sleep.

The bobcat is smaller than his Canadian relative, the Canada lynx, but he may still reach a hefty weight and even tip the scales at forty pounds. A normal-sized bobcat will average around twenty to twenty-five pounds. There is one on record shot by Kenneth E. Beveridge of Salem, New York, in 1957, that officially weighed thirty-six pounds. This cat was shot near a deer it had killed.

Bobcats average about three feet in length, and stand about two feet high at the shoulder. Their coat is light buff, dappled with black spots over most of the body and especially along the legs. The top of the four-to-six-inch tail is barred and only the top of the tip is black, not the entire tip, as in the case of the lynx. The underside of the animal, chin, and inside of legs are creamy white, as is the fur on the inside of the ears. The outer side of the ears is black with a big white patch in the center, a good identification mark in the woods.

The cheek hair is long and stands out from the face in a sort of ruff. The eyes are outlined in white, and the long whiskers are also white. The tips of the ears sometimes have a few long black hairs protruding from them, but not to the extent that the ears of the Canada lynx have them.

In desert country, where the background is naturally light, the cat has cleverly changed his color to nearly match the light sandy color of his surroundings. Desert wildcats are very light sandy buff with a minimum of dark areas. The noses of all bobcats are pinkish and the eyes yellow, as are those of all cats. Occasionally a jet-black bobcat is reported.

The bobcat feeds upon small animals, including rabbits, mice, rats, chipmunks, gophers, and birds, but it also turns to aquatic life when warm-blooded game is hard to find. It relishes poultry and young domestic livestock, kills young deer, and will even attack adult deer which are wounded, sick, or old and unable to move quickly. Sometimes deer bogged down in deep snow become food for the bobcat.

Its favorite method of hunting is to select a low branch over a game trail and stretch out along it, waiting for something to pass below. When bobcats decide to hunt this way, they always approach the tree from the opposite side and climb it there, so there are no telltale tracks to give them away. Lying along such a branch, they are high enough so that their scent is above any game below, and the added height makes a diving attack that more effective.

A friend of mine and a companion were hunting some years ago near Peekskill, New York, about fifty miles from New York City. They had sat down under a big pine to eat their lunch, opening their shotguns, as all good hunters do when not actually hunting. "Winnie" suddenly noticed that bits of bark and needles were dropping on him from above. At first he thought his friend was being funny, tossing them at him when he wasn't looking, but then realized they were coming from above him, down through the branches.

He slowly looked up, and there, a few feet above him, was

a big bobcat staring down at him with unblinking eyes as it flexed its claws along the bark of the branch. Winnie slowly put down his sandwich, closed his shotgun, and, without warning his companion, fired into the branches above him, then rolled aside.

Photograph by the author

Down came the cat, dead, just where he had been sitting, much to the horrified consternation of Winnie's unsuspecting companion, which goes to show that you never know who will drop in for lunch, even in the woods.

Bobcats are vicious fighters when cornered or attacked by dogs, fighting with such fury that they are called the "wild" cat. They will willingly take on a whole pack of dogs if no tree is handy, and usually the dogs will end up a pretty sorry bunch if they try to tangle with this chap.

The bobcat makes his den in rocky ledges and caves, sometimes taking over an abandoned fox's den if no other suitable place can be found. He uses hollow logs or a dense thicket if no natural cave can be found. The kittens are born in either early or late spring and stay with their mothers until fall. The father is given no part in their training, and after mating he usually wanders away again, leaving the mother to care for the approaching litter.

The kittens appear about sixty-three days after mating, and number from one to four, weighing about a dozen ounces each. After about ten days they open their eyes and begin to explore the den. They may nurse for two months until they are completely weaned. During the next few months they tag along after their mother, learning the business of being bobcats, and then, when the cooler months come around, they leave the family and go off to find their own territory and family. Bobcats mate at about a year old, and live for about fifteen years.

Like the lynx, the bobcat population varies with the amount of food available to them, and the cycle of the varying hare also affects the number of bobcats where the hare is their main source of food. These cats are a real help in keeping down the population of many small rodents which might be harmful to crops. Nearly 50 per cent of the bobcat's diet is estimated to be composed of such harmful mammals, as well as about 15 per cent of what might be called beneficial animals, and about 2 per cent of birds of all types. The remainder is made up of vegetables, refuse, dead animals, and birds and aquatic creatures they may eat when other food is hard to find.

Bobcats can leap as much as eight feet and are "quick as a cat" literally, but occasionally they are hit by cars while crossing the highway. I found one such traffic casualty in Georgia a while ago and so had a fine opportunity to photograph it to show the odd colorings of the ears. These cats, unlike the lynx, live in swamplands as well as desert country and do not require deep timber as a habitat. This bobcat, or "red lynx," as he is sometimes called, had been crossing from one swamp to another when he became another highway statistic, and a most unusual and interesting one.

23

These small wild cats sharpen their claws on tree trunks and stumps, and if you are in bobcat country you may find such trees or stumps with shreds of bark at the base. I have followed the tracks of these cats many times in both snow and soft dirt and they look like any house cat tracks at first glance.

The palm pads of the bobcat's feet are quite complicated. The front part of the palm pad has a double lobe, as does the heel pad as well. The feet do not develop long hair between the toes in winter, as do those of the lynx, so that the pads are quite plainly shown unless the snow is deep. I remember following one cat for miles when there was about a quarter inch of new snow over a heavy crust, perfect for tracking him. The stride of this cat was about eight inches to a foot and occasionally he would take a long bound, perhaps to keep his muscles limber or perhaps just for the fun of it. When he trotted, the stride was longer, and in one spot, where he ran after a partridge (which got away) he bounded along with nearly six feet between leaps.

In deeper snow, the tracks would have looked much larger, of course, and in soft mud along a swamp edge I've seen them apparently almost as big as those of the lynx. The normal track of a bobcat measures from one inch up to nearly two inches. The tracks of the females are somewhat smaller than those of the males and the hind feet of both are smaller than those of the front feet.

The bobcat, like the lynx, will often walk a log or even a stone wall if his trail crosses one. They poke their noses into holes in logs and under fallen trees, and will sometimes even come close to a farmhouse, watching it from the edge of the woods for some moments before going on about the business of finding a lunch or dinner. They usually stick pretty much to their own bailiwick, which may consist of four or five square miles of good hunting country.

Winter and summer they usually stay in their own territory unless a larger cat or civilization drives them further afield. In summer they bury their droppings, as do all cats, by clawing dirt over the spot, to conceal their presence in the area.

In spite of the inroads of civilizations into their territory, they seem able to adapt quite easily to new areas and are extending their range all the time. Not too many miles from any big city, if there is plenty of cover and food to be found, you can find their interesting tracks in the snow, or perhaps hear their wild concert during the mating season when they are romantically inclined.

Even if caught young, bobcats make poor pets, always remaining wild and untamed in spite of kindness and good care. They are often seen in zoos and wayside menageries, where they always seem to look out of place. To me a fleeting glimpse of a bobcat in the wilds is worth all the hours you could spend in front of a caged specimen put together. I am glad he is on the increase, for that means more people will perhaps be able to see this elusive backwoods cat in his native element, where he belongs and seems to be thriving better all the time.

EUROPEAN WILDCAT, *Felis silvestris*

Although not very common, the European Wildcat may still be found occasionally in England and in Scotland. It is not found in Ireland. It has been pushed further and further back into the wilderness areas of Europe, and while originally it ranged from Scotland across southern Europe to Asia Minor, it is extinct over most of this range today.

This cat is about the size of our own bobcat but has a longer and fluffier tail, barred with dark-brown or black marks. The back of the animal is dark, almost black, with spots visible on its sides and flanks. The throat is creamy white, and its lips and chin are also white. The forehead is marked with narrow stripes running from the eyes back over the crown, and the eyes are rimmed with white. It weighs around twenty to twenty-five pounds, although an old male in good health may tip the scales even higher. Females are smaller.

The tip of the tail is black on the top, as is that of *Lynx rufus,* our bobcat, but much fuller. Parts of the belly are also white in the male, but usually the female is not as strikingly marked as the male animal, perhaps for better concealment when taking care of her kittens.

The youngsters, from two to five, are born in a hollow tree or rocky den and are brought up much the same as all young kittens. The diet of this European bobcat is similar to that of our own, and his tracks are almost duplicates. They do not thrive well in captivity, being bad dispositioned and sullen. They do not live long once they have been caught and caged.

AFRICAN WILDCAT, *Felis lybica*

Africa, too, has its wildcat, and it is known by many and quite romantic names, including: "Kaffir cat," "Egyptian cat," "fettered cat," and "Booted cat." It ranges over all of Africa except the desert areas, as well as on Sardinia, the larger Mediterranean island, and at one time, centuries ago, on Gibraltar, for his fossilized bones have been discovered in deep cracks in the rock.

Including the twelve-inch tail, this cat is about three feet long, with the females a bit smaller. The tail is striped, and the back is marked with faint dark stripes running from side to side at regular intervals. The general color is a sandy gray, or pale buff, or cinnamon tan. The head is marked with small, narrow stripes, and the cheeks have short, dark stripes running back toward the neck.

The nose is pink, and the lips and chin are light—almost white, as is the chest and belly fur. The legs are faintly striped, like a tabby cat.

The diet of this cat consists of bush rats, hares, birds, and the young of antelope, sheep, and goats. He also will eat lizards, snakes, insects, and even tortoises in a pinch. In areas where poultry is raised, he lives high until caught, for chicken is his idea of the perfect meal, and he will pass up almost any other game for this fowl.

The home life of this relative of our bobcat is similar, as are the tracks, voice, and disposition. He weighs about as much as a small bobcat and as game is plentiful over most of his range, he seems to be thriving wherever found.

Thousands of years ago this cat was important to civilized man, who put him in high esteem. He was protected and worshiped, and temples were even erected in his honor for many years. He was buried with honor, even with royalty, but that is all over for this little feline now. Even though he is responsible for many of today's house cats, he is once more a creature of the wild, having to hunt for his meals like any other wildcat. Perhaps he even likes it better this way.

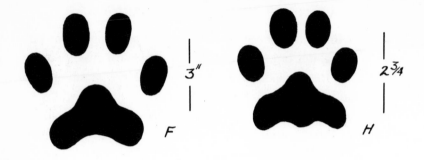

F 3"

H 2¾

$\mathcal{2}$. CANADA LYNX
Lynx canadensis

Driven northwards by civilization, the rarely seen Canada lynx is now found in numbers only in areas north of the Canadian border and in a few isolated spots in the United States. Only rarely has it been seen, trapped, or shot in the continental United States for many years. In Canada and Alaska, however, it still roams the wilderness on its huge, furry feet and silently lies in wait for its favorite prey, the varying hare.

The Canada lynx has several distinctive characteristics which set it apart from the bobcat of the United States and Canada. It is larger, standing over two feet high at the shoulders and weighing up to forty-four pounds. It is quite a few pounds heavier than the average bobcat but even the latter will attain lynx size upon occasion. The average weight of the lynx is about twenty-five to thirty pounds, a bit heavier than the bobcat.

The lynx is about three feet long plus a short, bobbed tail of about another four to six inches. The legs are long, and the

Photograph by Charles J. Ott, from National Audubon Society

feet, in proportion to the rest of the animal, are enormous. In winter they are heavily furred, especially between the toe pads. Thus the feet act as snowshoes, keeping the animal on top of deep snow. This enables it to successfully hunt the snowshoe rabbit even when the snow is deep in the tall timber.

This timberland cat is lighter in color than the bobcat, and the fur is longer, thicker, and less peppered with dark spots. The tail is black over the entire tip, not just across the top, as is that of the bobcat. The ears are edged with black and tipped with long tufts of black hair which stand up for over an inch; a most distinctive trade-mark of all the lynx family.

The eyes, in adults, are bright yellow, but in the kittens the eyes are bright blue. When we were camping in the beautiful Mont Tremblant Park in Canada while doing research for this book, two of these kittens were captured by the park personnel near where we camped. They were mighty cute little tykes and soon became used to civilized fare of cat meat, milk, and small fish caught for them by the park staff.

In the introduction there is a picture of a young gentleman, Pierre Coutu, son of the park director, Captain Maurice Coutu, who is holding one of these little chaps, and you will note that even at this estimated age of about a month the kitten has the characteristic ear tufts, black-edged ears and black tail tip—what there is of it. There were four of these little kittens, apparently abandoned by their mother, but two got away. The two which were captured are to go to the big zoo in Quebec City for all to see.

At night these two little cats produced the weirdest chorus of calls, squalls, and screeches, some of which were almost bird-like in tone. After many attempts I finally got them down on tape, and even at this age they would make your hair curl if heard late at night in the woods. The adults do even better, especially during the mating season, when their voices reach the peak of volume and discord. Besides uttering these wild cries, the lynx snarls, hisses, and emits a low growl when eating, but like all cats is a silent hunter.

The color of the lynx is more gray than tawny, with brown mottlings. Its cheek hair is long and has mixed color of gray-black and white. The white whiskers are long and sensitive, enabling the cat to judge the size of any opening it may wish to pass through. The long cheek hair stands out from the side of the face in a sort of ruff, another good identification mark of the animal when you see him in the woods.

The favorite food of the lynx is the varying hare or snowshoe rabbit, and as the population of this animal varies, so does the lynx population. This big hare changes color with the season—

brown in summer and white in winter—and about every seven to ten years the population declines, and so does the number of lynx, an important matter to trappers of the north country. Lynx also eat grouse, ptarmigan, rodents, and even snakes and songbirds if other game is hard to find. They can follow game by scent as well as by sight and ear, and swim after it if need be. They climb trees well, and one of their favorite ways of hunting is to lie on a branch over a game trail ready to pounce upon anything that happens to pass below them. The lynx is not as eager to attack large game as is the bobcat and seldom attacks deer except perhaps when fawns are about. He may also attack the young of caribou or bighorn sheep in areas where the two animals live together. Occasionally a lynx has been known to leap down upon something he would have been smarter to let pass unattacked.

For example, my mother was a Whitcomb from Vermont, and in reading the Whitcomb family history I came across a quite unusual lynx anecdote. Back in 1725 one of the family, named Isaac Jones, one of the first to leave the Massachusetts Bay Colony for the Green Mountains, and lived up there with his family in a cabin. His nearest neighbor was about five miles away through the deep woods, but one day his wife needed a cauldron-kettle, as they were called, in which to make soft soap. These were big iron kettles which sat upon three pointed legs about six inches long, to keep the kettle up above the hot coals of the fireplace. Isaac, being six feet six inches tall and afraid of neither man nor beast, said he would walk over to the neighbors to get one for his wife.

He did this, got the kettle, and started back late in the afternoon. As the kettle was heavy to lug, he decided to put it over his head, resting the brim on his broad shoulders. This he did, peering out from under it from time to time to check the trail ahead.

Almost home, and passing under some low branches, he was suddenly struck down by a terrific blow on top of the kettle. Scrambling to his feet, he looked about for his assailant and some sort of weapon with which to defend himself. None was needed, for he had been wearing a most effective one on his head. On the ground beside the trail lay the kettle, and impaled upon one of the legs was a very dead lynx. This was one time the lynx forgot to really look before he leaped.

Canada lynx den in a hollow log or rocky cave, and about three months after mating, one to four kittens are born. They are light tan in color, spotted, and occasionally blotched with brown. They may be born either blind or with eyes open (some say they are blind for ten days). In two hours they can stand and soon afterwards stagger about the cave. After being completely weaned at about three months, they go hunting with their mother. Sometimes the whole family is together, with the little kittens bumbling along behind, full of curiosity and not much hunting sense.

After about a year, they go off on their own, although some may leave earlier if the urge to see what's over the next ridge gets the better of them. They hunt mostly at night, or at least by dusk, but when food is hard to find they are on the prowl by daylight as well as by moonlight.

The track of the lynx is especially large, about the size of a mountain lion's print. In winter the feet are heavily furred, as I mentioned, but in summer they shed much of this and the tracks appear smaller, but still much too big for a cat of this size. It's odd, but some lynx skins I have examined, taken in November, have been bare of this foot fur, and others I have checked, taken in October, have had fur an inch long between the toes. It probably depends upon the coldness of the weather where taken and the depth of snow on the ground, rather than the time of year. Lynx tracks measure about three inches in length.

The palm pads are less complicated than those of the smaller bobcat, with the anterior edge of the palm pad single-lobed, instead of double-lobed like the bobcat. None of the claws show, and the straddle (distance between left and right feet) is less than that of the mountain lion. In the case of the latter, the tail drag also shows in deep snow, while the only way a lynx can leave a tail mark is to sit down!

The trail of a hunting lynx is most interesting to follow as it has some fascinating and unusual characteristics. The lynx, like a small boy, must apparently walk upon any fallen log it comes to, hardly ever passing one up and even at times seeming to go out of its way to locate one to walk on. Perhaps it likes the added height from which to look around, or perhaps, like the small boy, it does it just because the log is there.

Another odd thing to notice when following a lynx trail is that once in a while the cat will make a great leap of ten feet or more, apparently just for the fun of it, or to keep in training. It may be to confuse a possible enemy following it or to bewilder folks who write about it.

About the only enemy the Canada lynx has, other than man and his traps and guns, is the porcupine. Occasionally a lynx will tackle one of these "quill pigs" of the timberlands and promptly wish he hadn't. Many a lynx has died as a result of this foolishness, for unlike the Fisher, who knows how to handle the porcupine safely, the lynx hasn't learned the trick.

The lynx and the smaller bobcat are the only wild cats found in the New World with short tails, and they are really short. That of the bobcat is a bit longer in proportion to that of the lynx, but neither is more than six inches in length. The tail of the lynx appears even shorter due to the thicker hair.

Originally the Canada lynx could be found over most of the United States along the Canadian border, but now it is rarely seen except in Canada and Alaska. It seems a shame that we have practically lost such an interesting and picturesque citizen, but at least he's not too far away, and we still have him in numbers in our forty-ninth state, Alaska. Long may he prowl and yowl!

My friend, Vincent Nestor, the keeper of small animals at the New York Zoological Park, once raised a bobcat and a lynx together and displayed them in the same cage, where for many years they lived in complete harmony. They had been brought up together as kittens, and, although not close friends, they were at least willing to be compatible. Vincent told me that a captured adult lynx is treacherous and may attack at any time, and it apparently remembers well anyone who has mistreated it in the past.

There are several types of lynx in the Old World as well as here in the New World. A lynx similar to the Canada lynx once roamed over most of Europe except the Mediterranean countries. Now only a few survive in the alps of Scandinavia and northern Russia. They are classified as *Lynx lynx* and known as the northern lynx. Similar animals are also found in Siberia and Tibet. In the Himalayan Mountains they are found above ten thousand feet. Some of these are also found in Asia and Africa.

In Africa the caracal (*Felis caracal*) also appears to be lynx-like in appearance, although it has a chestnut-reddish coat. It, too, has the long ear tufts and black tail tip. The ears are white inside and black outside, and the eyes are rimmed with white. This animal, unlike our Canada lynx, used to be tamed for the hunt by wealthy Indians and was kept as a rather uncertain pet in some households. In hunting, the caracal could run down a gazelle and even catch birds by leaping into the air and knocking them down with its paws.

Somehow, regardless of appearance, nothing looks quite like a lynx to me but the animal we find up north on our own continent.

Photograph by New York Zoological Society

3. CHEETAH
Acinonyx jubatus

$3\frac{1}{2}''$ F

$3\frac{1}{4}''$ H

There is always one exception to any rule, and the cheetah, or hunting leopard, is just that when it comes to the general rules of the family of wild cats. It looks more like a dog than a cat, its claws are not as fully retracted as those of other cats, and, unlike most of them, it can be really tamed and led about with a collar and chain and taught to hunt for its master. Otherwise it's a true member of the Felidae family, in fine standing.

Cheetahs are found in Asia and Africa. The Asian cheetah (*Acinonyx venatica*) is spotted, as is the African cheetah (*Acinonyx jubatus*). Another African ·species (*Acinonyx rex*) is striped. The one shown in the photo (*A. jubatus*) ranges from India to the Caspian Sea and on southward into Africa from the northern Transvaal to Cape Colony. All types are very similar, running to a length of seven feet including tail and weighing up to about 138 pounds. Their basic color is tawny brown with black spots or stripes. A heavy, dark line runs from the inner corners of their keen eyes down to the corners of their mouths, as though painted there, and bluish streaks mark the sides of their faces. The nose is black, and the tail is both spotted and ringed. They stand high on long, slender legs, and the height at the shoulder is about three feet. The neck seems unexpectedly short. A short mane covers their shoulders, and this can be raised when they are startled or sighting game.

The spots of the cheetah are very small and all about the same size rather than in blotches. These are found not only on the yellowish back and sides but along the edges of the creamy white throat and undersides and inner leg surfaces. These serve as fine camouflage for the hunting animal.

The main claim to fame, besides its most uncatlike appearance, is the great speed of this amazing animal. The long, slender legs and hard, tough paw pads, are ideally designed for pursuit of its quarry in the open country, where it lives and hunts. From a standing start after a silent stalk, the cheetah can spurt in two seconds to forty-five miles an hour, and then race five hundred yards at up to seventy miles an hour if need be. No fleeing animal can escape such a charge by speed alone, for there is no animal as fast in the world as this cat.

Cheetahs have especially keen eyesight and hunt by this instead of by scent, being able to spot game a mile or more away. For hundreds of years these cats have been trained to hunt game for royalty, and they usually hunt in pairs, stalking together, charging together, and boxing the game between them so there is no chance for escape. While working together in this way, the animals give odd, birdlike calls, apparently as signals between them.

When they reach their victim, they hit it to the ground with a paw and then seize its throat. They kill by strangulation, as their claws are not very effective for tearing, and so hold their prey until dead. If they are trained hunters, they release the dead animal and are rewarded with a cup of its blood for the kill.

Hunting cheetahs are usually hooded like falcons, with the hoods removed when the game is sighted, often at a great distance. Once released, the two cats use every bit of cover to conceal themselves until they are within a hundred yards or so of their intended victim, when they leap forward and it's all over in a matter of seconds.

These unusual cats are tamed quite easily and purr like big tabby cats when stroked by their masters. They will follow their owners around the house like pet dogs and are only vicious or treacherous if they have been mistreated. A pair of these cats used to live at the New York Zoological Society's Bronx Zoo. They were so friendly that it was a problem to clean their enclosure, for they kept rubbing against the keeper to be petted and getting in the way of the broom.

Although cheetahs do not spend as much time in the trees as do others of the cat family, they can climb well if necessary, and sometimes, when suddenly surprised, will take to a handy tree rather than to flight, for which they are far better suited. They do, however, keep their claws sharp by scratching them on a tree, often traveling some distance to get to a favorite scratching post or tree. Unfortunately, these posts are soon spotted by native hunters and trappers, who promptly set snares there to catch them.

The food of the cheetah ranges from small game up to the kudu, an antelope as large as a horse. Occasionally a whole family of cheetahs will hunt together, from four to six or more in all. The youngsters, from two to four in number, are born at almost any time of the year, as are the offspring of most tropical cats.

The kittens or cubs are silky, and unlike their parents are blue-gray on the upper parts and creamy white below. After several weeks, the dark coat begins to change in color, and the black spots or stripes begin to become visible. Once the baby coat and color have changed to that of the parent, the kittens begin to join the parents on practice hunting trips and soon are racing along almost as fast as their elders. A family of hunting cheetahs roaming the open plains bodes ill for any game that cannot either fly or burrow. In the latter case that may be no escape either, for one or more of the cats may wait for it to reappear.

The tracks of this unusual animal are quite uncatlike, for the claws register in the tracks like dog foot prints. The front paws are a bit wider than those of the hind feet and measure about three and a half-inches long. These cats cover eight feet at a bound, and the tracks do not register on top of each other as the animal speeds along.

The voice of the cheetah is catlike, with the addition of the "chirping" noises which they use between themselves when hunting, and an especially loud purr they produce when happy, well fed and contended. The purr is similar to that of a tame cat but the volume is turned way up. When fighting, the cheetah can snarl with the best of the felines, but he is not a noisy animal, and stalks silently and surely, saving his breath for the final fatal dash.

Cheetahs have for centuries been the pets of royalty and the wealthy, but even now an occasional Hollywood-type character is seen strolling along with a leashed cheetah in tow; actually, being led by a cheetah might be more correct. These cats are often used in movies as stage dressing for spectacular productions, because they are easy to handle and reliable in disposition. They usually live to an age of about sixteen years.

One often wonders just where in the early dim dawn of evolution such contradictions of animal development came about, and why; how an animal more doglike than catlike turned out to be a feline after all. Regardless of how it came about, the cheetah is one of nature's most interesting children, and as is so often the case, the exception which proves the rule (in this case of cats) also proves to be of perhaps more interest than the "rule."

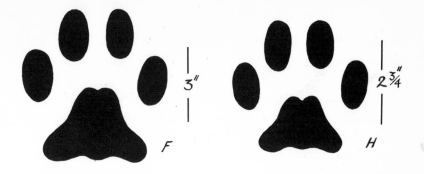

F   3″   H   2¾″

4. CLOUDED LEOPARD
Felis nebulosa

Of all the cat family, perhaps the most unusually marked and most rarely seen in zoos is the clouded leopard, which roams the wastelands of northern India, Burma, Tibet, Sumatra, Java, and Borneo. Not related directly to the common leopard, although there is nothing ever "common" about any leopard, the clouded leopard resembles in many ways the extinct saber-toothed tiger, for he has the longest tusks or canine teeth for his size of any of the Felidae family.

These tusks are greatly prized by the natives of Borneo known as the Kayans, who use them for decorations and will pay high prices for them. They used to be worn only by those who had taken a human head, but as that hobby is frowned upon in this day and age, now almost any native who can afford to buy one does so. They have a value of about twenty-five dollars in our money, a veritable fortune for a native.

Photograph by Al Liebeck

The clouded leopard has other interesting characteristics besides these extra-long tusks. His coat is extremely fancy, for it has the rosettes of the jaguar, the spots of the leopard, and the stripes of the tiger, all in one piece of material. His basic body color is a grayish yellow above and creamy white below. The back and sides of this interesting cat are marked with almost "square" rosettes, edged with black, fading into the yellowish gray of the coat. The white lower parts are spotted with dark-brown or black blotches while the heavy tail is

42

spotted and banded. Smaller spots ornament his head and legs, and stripes run lengthwise on his powerful neck. His ears are black-edged, and his cheeks carry dark blotches running from front to back. All in all, with his white lips and chin and snowy whiskers and pink nose, he is about as flashy a wild creature as you can find.

This six-foot animal stands about eighteen inches high at the shoulder and may weigh up to a hundred pounds. One fine skin I examined from India was seventy-eight inches long, over six feet, and the animal would have stood about seventeen inches high. Another from Yenping, China, measured seventy-two inches long. The latter skin showed long fur between the toes, and the magnificent tail was long and very fluffy. It measured eleven inches around the thickest part, and it was heavily furred for the entire three-foot length.

The natives of Borneo prize this pelt for seat mats, and it's no wonder, for a more exotic seat could hardly be found. Personally I prefer to think of the original owner sitting in it himself.

The clouded leopard spends much, if not most, of his time in the trees, and there he has the most uncatlike habit of building large nests of sticks and leaves, similar to those our American black bears build in beech trees. It has been reported that these big cats use these nests for both sleeping and as blinds in which they can lie in wait for an unwary monkey or bird who might venture too close.

Usually these gaily coated cats avoid man like a plague, but upon occasion they have attacked and killed a human being, either from great hunger, by mistaking him for an animal, or perhaps from being injured so that the animal could not catch more suitable and more agile food.

Known by such names as "tortoise-shell tiger," "tree leopard," and the "tiger of the forked branch" by the Malayans, it is easy to understand how the clouded leopard has the habit of lying flat on a tree branch waiting for game to pass below. When hunting in this way, his coat blends perfectly with the leaves and lights and shadows of the jungle, and he is practically invisible. The Chinese refer to him as the "mint leopard," pointing out that his odd-shaped rosettes resemble the leaves of a local mint tree.

Photograph by Al Liebeck

His young, usually two to four, are born in a hollow tree whenever possible, or a hollow log, or, if neither can be found when the female's time arrives, she will have her litter in some secluded thicket as far from prying eyes as possible. The kittens are kept with the mother until they are able to hunt for themselves, and then they gradually wander off to find a territory of their own and a mate. If caught quite young, this cat can be tamed and makes a rather good pet. He bears watching when

44

adult, though, as he may revert to the wild and become savage. When kept in a zoo, the cats are quite delicate and require special treatment, including a high and uniform temperature to match that of their homeland.

Their food in the wilds consists of small mammals, particularly arboreal species, monkeys, birds, and even small reptiles when other food is difficult to find. One of their favorite birds is the peacock, large enough to provide a really sizable dinner.

Photograph by Al Liebeck

The track of this cat—when you can find it on the ground, which is rare—measures about three inches long. The hind feet are a bit smaller. He uses tree trunks and branches as scratching posts, and has the habit of lying on a branch with his short legs hanging down on either side when resting. If lying in wait for a possible dinner below, his feet are curled under him on the branch, poised for the spring and attack. He is an excellent climber and very much at home in all types of trees.

45

The feet of this cat are equipped with very small toe pads and a five-lobed palm pad. Interestingly enough, in examining dozens of study skins of cats of all kinds, it was not unusual to find that the palm and heel pads of some of them varied even on the same cat. Some had single and some had double anterior lobes on the larger pads and some varied even as to size. That's what keeps this business of presenting a "typical" track open to controversy, and introduces some fine arguments.

The voice of the clouded leopard is like the standard variety of cats with no outstanding qualities that I can find, such as the "woof" of the tiger and the scream of the mountain lion. Actually not too much is known about the home life of this elusive wildcat, but it's nice to know that such a colorful and interesting "nest builder" does exist, even if on the other side of the globe. If you live near a zoo that is lucky enough to have one of the little "saber-toothed" tigers of the trees, be sure to spend some time looking at him, for you are looking at a rare and exotic member of the Felidae family.

Photograph by New York Zoological Society

5. FISHING CAT
Felis viverrina

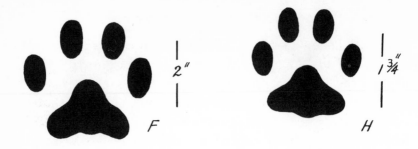

F   2″   H   1¾″

Looking very much like an alley cat cornered by a neighborhood pooch on the back fence, the fishing cat of India and southern China arches its back and dares the intruder to come closer. If the intruder is smart at all, he will keep his distance, for the fishing cat is a savage fighter and a skillful one.

If a dog ever comes across this particular type of wild cat in its native land, he'd better have some stout reinforcements along or beat a hasty retreat, for in spite of its small size, this wild feline has been known to attack and kill a leopard almost twice its size, despite the latter's own reputation for savagery.

This interesting feline is almost as mysterious as the reason why they call him the "fishing cat." Certainly all cats love fish, but no cat lives almost exclusively on the finny sort of dinner expected from this cat's name. He undoubtedly does eat fish but certainly not exclusively, for in zoos he is fed meat, as are the rest of the cats, and seems to thrive on it.

Unfortunately, the natives of the areas in which he is found are not particularly interested in the habits of the wildlife, and so there is no great amount of information to be had on this feline. The fishing cat is found along the banks of lakes, rivers, and swamps, and so is assumed to live on fish and to catch most of his meals with his own built-in fishing hooks, his claws. As a result of this, the natives call him a real fishing cat.

His den is usually in a deep thicket away from the water's

edge, in a hollow log, or in a small natural cave. Cats are not diggers and so seldom will you find them in a burrow, as you might a fox, wolf, or other true digger. The dens are hard to find, for this cat lives away from civilization and is very elusive.

The animal is about forty-two inches long, including the tail; he stands about fifteen inches high, and weighs around seventeen pounds. He has a short-legged silhouette, and his coat is grayish brown with brown or black spots scattered over his body and legs in no particular pattern. The cheeks are marked with white and black areas, and his nose is pinkish.

The eyes are rimmed with white, and the lips, chin, belly, and throat are lighter but still marked with spots. The tail, longer than that of a bobcat, is barred and darker toward the tip. Dark bars run backwards from the eyes over the forehead to the back, where they break up into spots. The white whiskers emerge from rows of dark spots on the upper lips, as in many another cat of similar size and coloring.

The natives where this cat lives give him a very bad reputation indeed, claiming that he not only lives on fish, small mammals, and birds, but is also a calf killer, a dog killer, and even an animal that will carry off human babies left unguarded.

It is doubtful that he deserves such a reputation, but perhaps isolated instances have occurred that have served as a basis for these tales. Perhaps larger cats have been guilty, with the small fishing cat reaping the blame for the deed. At any rate, the natives hate and fear him and hunt him whenever possible, and the tales of his vile deeds are told and retold with no loss of details in the stories.

The tracks of the animal are typically catlike, with four toes showing on all four feet. The pads are small, and the track measures about one and three-quarters inches long, or perhaps a bit longer in a big old male. The females are slightly smaller, as in most species of cats. The tracks are to be found in the mud of river, lake, and stream banks, near rice paddies, and occasionally even close to native huts where he might find food. The claws do not show in the tracks unless the fishing cat is fighting, or perhaps frightened and has his claws extended in preparation for defense.

The voice of the fishing cat is that of any other cat of similar size, a collection of snarls and hisses, and, when looking for a mate, a wild chorus of yowls and screeches, apparently of great allure to a possible mate.

The kittens, from one to four, but usually twins, are born in the warmest part of the year and arrive hungry and blind. They are nursed for several weeks before they begin to take interest in more solid foods brought home by the mother. Later, they are taught to fish and hunt with their elders, and after about ten months they wander off to seek mates and set up housekeeping on their own.

Not very much is known about the home life of this Old World cat, and he is not too common in zoos. Apparently the natives have less interest in his life and habits than in eliminating him. As a result, this interesting cat is still quite a mystery in many departments.

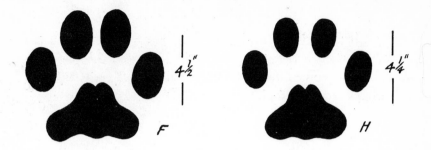

F   H

6. JAGUAR
Felis onca

This is our heaviest American cat, and it ranges from Argentina to the southern parts of Texas and New Mexico. It was once found in California, and occasionally has been reported in southern Arizona and New Mexico. It is truly a big cat, weighing up to three hundred pounds and standing nearly thirty inches at the shoulder.

The length is well over seven feet, and some have been recorded up to nine feet in length. The tail may be two and a half feet long, proportionately shorter than that of the leopard, and quite thick and heavy. The body is chunky and quite heavy compared with the mountain lion or cheetah.

The coat is a really sporty combination of yellow, black, and white, resembling that of the leopard, but with big, well defined rosettes, many of which have an added spot in the center, a sort of trade-mark of this big cat. The head is peppered with small spots, and even the creamy white throat, chest, and belly,

Photograph by New York Zoological Society

as well as the inside of the legs, are also spotted. Spots on the legs and underside are bigger than those on the rest of the body and are real spots instead of rosettes. The tail is decorated with big rosettes instead of bars or stripes. The underside of the tail is whitish.

The lips and chin of the cat are also creamy white, and the ears are short, rounded, and well furred inside and out, with white fur on the inside. The paws are white with a spattering of small spots.

JAGUAR — *Felis onca*

He is a startlingly colored beast, but living mainly as he does in the tropics, the coloring makes ideal camouflage in the sunlight-flecked foliage where he lurks. In any other area and against any other background he would certainly go hungry much of the time.

The jaguar hunts both by lying in wait over a game trail and by stalking on the ground, and his diet ranges from rodents to ranch cattle, including guinea pigs, deer, sheep, alpaca, llamas, capybara, peccaries, and tapirs. If these are hard to find, he will dig up turtle eggs, battle a crocodile, or splash fish out of the water where he can grab it on dry land. Unlike the majority of cats, he really loves the water and is an expert swimmer, often going in to cool off, escape insects, or apparently just for the fun of it and a bit of fishing.

He is very fond of domestic animals, killing full grown oxen, mules, and horses with comparative ease. The frontier areas of South America are full of tales of jaguar raids on cattle, horses, and even their human owners. He has been reported as many times having gone out of his way to attack human beings. Sometimes this is a bad mistake, particularly if the chap happens to be Sasha Siemel, a fellow member of the Adventurers Club of New York.

Sasha's hobby, as well as profession, has been killing jaguars with either bow and arrow or a special spear he designed. He believes firearms give man an unfair advantage, so he tackles these great cats on foot on the ground, using just a spear in claw-to-spear mortal combat. For years he has been hired by ranchers in the state of Matto Grosso in Brazil to protect their cattle from raids by this swashbuckling feline, and so far he has eliminated nearly 250 of these cats. His opinion of *el tigre* (the tiger), as the jaguar is known to the natives and ranchers, is one of great respect, and by now the feeling must be mutual.

This fine member of the Felidae family is a bold animal, often

53

living close to civilization, where it will find domestic animals handy. There are several species of jaguars, all looking more or less alike and varying but slightly in size and suit, depending upon where they are found. In contradiction to the mountain lion (*Felis cougar*), the warmer the climate, the larger and heavier the jaguar grows, with the largest being found in the deepest and hottest jungles. He prefers to live near water.

The voice of the jaguar is seldom heard, for most of the time he does his hunting in silence. When you do hear his voice it is unmistakable, like the sawing cough of the leopards. The jaguar emits a hoarse, grunting sound, which is difficult to describe, let alone spell. About the nearest you can come to it is an "Ugh, ugh, ugh, ugh!" which by no means does it justice. The next time you are at a zoo at feeding time perhaps you'll have a chance to hear a jaguar make a few such comments about the quality of the horse meat. You will always remember it. He also snarls, growls, and has other cattish expressions.

The young of the big cat are born in the spring (in the cooler areas) about a hundred days after mating in January. In the hotter parts of the animal's range they may be born at almost any time of the year, as there is no regular seasonal mating period. There are usually two to four kittens or cubs, and they are well furred at birth but blind. They soon develop into lively little tykes, and after weaning they go hunting with their parents. In many instances, both parents help bring up the youngsters, but the mother is generally in charge of this domestic phase of a cat's life. Occasionally a pure-black melanistic kitten arrives with the standard model, but it is accepted along with the others without any great fuss and given a seat at the "table." These grow into exotic "black panthers," but you can always see the rosettes under certain light, for a jaguar is still a jaguar even when disguised as one's shadow.

Jaguar kittens stay with their mother for considerable time, often still hunting with her when two years old, when a new litter takes their place in her attentions. By that time they are big and powerful and can fend for themselves. A full-grown jaguar can easily drag a full-grown horse for a mile to a place where this meal can be consumed at the cat's leisure.

The tracks of the big cat are typically catlike and may measure four and a half or five inches in length. The tracks are often quite deeply impressed in soft ground along riverbanks, for the weight of the cat really sinks his feet into the mud. On dry ground and along well-traveled game trails the tracks are hard to spot, but wherever the ground is soft or damp, *el tigre's* tracks are easy to recognize due to their size and catlike appearance. Sometimes at the base of a tree you can find especially deep tracks where he crouched to leap upward into low branches, or stood while scratching the bark to sharpen his claws.

The finding of jaguar tracks near a native settlement fills the natives with dread, for all fear this great hunting cat—not only for the safety of their livestock and pets, but for themselves as well. Ancient Mexicans regarded the big cat as sacred, and many statues have been found depicting the jaguar in many forms. South American folk tale and legend is full of references to this huge and colorful cat. Some are a bit difficult to take seriously.

For example, one of the popular ones explains that the jaguar sprawls out on a limb and drops its tail into the water for the fish to bite; then, when the fish has a good hold, the animal flicks it onto the bank or into the air, to be neatly caught in the paws or mouth. That I would certainly enjoy seeing myself.

Other tales, more easily believed, tell of how, during flood periods, the animal will hunt along the riverbanks for natives huddled on rooftops or marooned in trees, swimming out to attack them, or climb into boats containing cattle, livestock or humans. This may very well be true, for the big cat is bold, loves the water, is intelligent, resourceful, and always hungry.

In years past, before professional hunters were employed to help balance the scales, as many as six thousand head of prime cattle were lost every year to jaguars. Since then their numbers have been decreased by hunters and trappers (both for pelts and zoos) down to a point where they are far fewer in amount except in the deep jungles, where they are of no danger to man and his property.

The last one killed in Texas was in 1946, in Arizona in 1949, and the last one reported killed in California was taken in 1860 near Palm Springs. This does not mean that they are not still about in those states; the cats are learning better how to elude man and many of his contraptions.

Although the jaguar may be vanishing from north of the Mexican border, it is still found in numbers in the hot jungles to the south. Let's hope that there will always be some of these sporty cats stalking through the forest paths, swimming the rivers, and, according to legend, fishing with their tails in quiet pools. There is too much excitement under that colorful coat to lose forever. Whether called by the scientific name, or by such names as: "spotted king cat," "ringtailed panther," "American leopard," "American tiger" or "Mexican tiger," he's a fine addition to the wildlife of this continent's countryside.

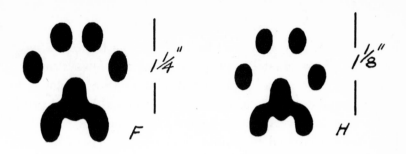

F   1/4"

H   1/8"

7. JAGUARUNDI
Felis yaguarundi

One day recently I was standing in the "red-light house" in New York City's Bronx Zoo, watching two of these small cats galloping around their enclosure, when a man and two youngsters joined me in the dim light of the building. (This house is dark, and the enclosures where the nocturnal small animals are kept are lighted by dim red light so that they are active, and you can watch them in motion rather than asleep, as they would be in bright light.)

The two youngsters watched with standard small-fry excitement and interest, firing innumerable questions at their father beside me. He stared up at the name sign over the glass, and I could see his lips move as he tried to pronounce it. After a few moments of frustration, he said: "Come on, fellows, it's just a couple of cats," and hauled away the boys, who were still spouting questions.

True, they were a couple of cats, but not *just* cats, for these

Photograph by New York Zoological Society

"miniature lions" are quite unusual and rarely seen even in our southern states, where they live. They are found from Brazil up through Central America, Mexico, and into southern Texas, and perhaps into parts of New Mexico.

There are two phases of this interesting cat. First is the typical gray phase in which the animal is all gray except for two small, light spots beside the nose on the upper lips and possibly a lighter area on the chest. Usually it is solid gray. The other, or red phase, is called the *eyra,* and it wears a reddish brown coat with a white throat and lips. The *eyra,* oddly enough for a cat, has red whiskers to match its coat.

The gray phase and red phase both belong to the same breed of cat, but until a few years ago they were believed to be different species. Both are found in a single litter, which proves that they are the same cat but just dressed in different coats, as are the black and brown phases of our black bear, which can arrive in either color coat.

Here, too, the zoologists appear to be further confused, for some refer to this cat as the *Felis cacomitli*, while others stick with *Felis yaguarundi*, even spelling it *yagouaroundi* in some publications.

This little cat runs to about fifty inches in length, including an especially long tail which may measure almost half the length of the entire animal. He stands about a foot high at the shoulder and weighs from ten to twenty pounds. The short legs and long body of the animal, particularly in the gray phase, make you think a little of the otter, hence the frequent use of the name "otter cat." The jaguarundi is about twice the size of the ordinary house cat.

His fur is sleek and short, and the animal is often found near water, where he hunts for birds in the reeds and marsh grass. He hunts for fish, frogs, birds, and many small animals, including rabbits and even young deer, as reported in Paraguay. He also eats insects and reptiles when hard pressed for a meal. He swims well and catches rats and mice about rice fields. In fact, he is said to be such a good swimmer that he catches fish with ease. He also climbs well and unlike many cats hunts by day as well as by night.

The jaguarundi is particularly wary of man and lives in thick vegetation. Thus he is seldom seen, even in areas where he is known to thrive. His fur is poor and so has little value to hunters and trappers.

Although frequently exhibited in zoos, he does not make a good pet. He has been tamed upon occasion, but normally remains suspicious of his keeper, hissing and spitting even years later, as though just captured.

As he spends most of his life close to water, a most unlikely place to find any member of the Felidae family, the jaguarundi's den is almost impossible to locate. It is probably some distance back from the water—under a bank, in a deep thicket, or possibly in a small cave.

In the tropics, the young may be born at any time of the year, and they have been seen at almost any period from August to the following March, which would indicate that breeding takes place over a wide range of months, even over the whole year. They number from one to four, but usually there are twins or possibly three in a litter and, as already mentioned both red and gray kittens will be found in one batch.

Not much is known about the weaning and training of these little wild cats, but probably they are weaned at about a month and taught to hunt with their mother until able to go off alone and find their own mates and territory.

They have particular value as pest controllers around rice fields, where rats and mice do great damage to the crops. They are so much at home in the water, being able to cross rivers and ponds quite easily, that they also hunt successfully in the rice fields.

One interesting characteristic about these little cats is that they quite literally "pale with anger." The dark-tipped hairs of the gray phase are lighter close to the body and so, when the cat is angered or badly frightened, it bristles its hair and the lighter portions come into view, actually making the animal a paler color than when relaxed with the fur closer to the body.

The tracks of this intriguing small cat are about one inch long, although I have measured many jaguarundi feet in which they varied from less than an inch long to nearly an inch and a half. They have small pads, and the palm pad is quite simple. The tracks of the hind feet are about an eighth of an inch shorter than those of the front feet. The feet of the females may be smaller than those of the males. Tracks can be found along marshes and riverbanks, in the dust away from the water where they go to hunt, and around posts where they sharpen their claws. They walk almost perfectly in their own tracks, like most silent stalkers, but can cover several feet at a bound when pursuing game or escaping from an enemy.

Although not particularly bothered by man, except where their numbers are excessive, they are preyed upon by larger members of the cat family, and only their agility and ability to escape through small openings and into the water can save them. Fortunately they are hard to catch, so there seems to be no fear of their becoming a vanishing species.

The jaguarundi voice is a mixture of snarls, hisses, and other cattish noises. The cat is a ferocious fighter when cornered and snarls and spits when frightened like any tomcat threatened by a dog. When young, he makes almost birdlike "chirps," as does a baby lynx.

It is doubtful that you will ever see one in the wild, but if you are down near the border of Mexico or further south and see what looks like an exceptionally big red or gray house cat with a mighty long tail, you may have seen one of these odd animals. If you happen to have one cornered, and he snarls and turns paler while you watch, you may be sure about his breed, and in spite of his small size and pussycat look, you'd better give him all the room he needs to get away.

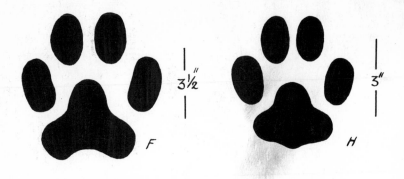

F   3½"   3"   H

8. LEOPARD
Felis pardus

Ever since I began to read about animals as a youngster, I've been thrilled at the many tales about leopards. This species of big cat may be found in Asia from Malaya to Siberia to the Black Sea, on Sumatra and Java, as well as throughout Africa. About all of Africa except the Sahara Desert can be called home for this sinister cat.

Foot for foot and pound for pound, leopards are the most feared and destructive of all the big cats. In India a price has been on their heads, and as many as five thousand a year have been killed there. Unfortunately, women admire their spotted coats for themselves, and at present the leopard is in danger of being exterminated in many areas. This has a double-barreled bad result. Not only are we losing a great and colorful animal, but, where it has been killed off, the population of pigs and

Photograph by New York Zoological Society

baboons has increased alarmingly, and the farmers in those areas now suffer great losses due to these two animals.

In the dim past, leopards also ranged over Europe as far west as Spain and even in Great Britain, but civilization has pushed this big cat further and further back into his present range, where his coughing warning still strikes terror to man and beast.

The leopard family includes species which range from some as small as five feet long up to really big cats of over eight feet or more in length. All have the same general build and characteristic spots. Even the melanistic "black leopard" has the spots, which can be seen in a certain light. These black leopards are found most commonly in Asia—in China and Malaya. Both regular and black kittens can be born in the same litter, proving they are the same species of cat under the skin.

The usual leopard color is a tawny yellow above and creamy white below, with a complete network of black spots like paw prints spattered all over him. On the back and sides these spots are in the form of rough circles with a shaded center. The spots on the head and legs are smaller, and the lips, chin, and chest are usually free of spots except for a few scattered ones. The leopards of Africa seem to have smaller and more definite spots, rather than rosettes. Oddly enough, no black leopards have been recorded from Africa.

No matter what coat the big cats wear, it serves as perfect camouflage for their hunting technique. Their favorite method of attack is to lie in waiting above a game trail where animals may pass close below. At other times, they will stalk a victim and then make a sudden, furious charge for the last few feet, to bring him down once he is within range. They kill by seizing a victim's throat and tearing it with their forepaws.

After a kill, they frequently drag the carcass high into a tree, where it will be safe from others and can be eaten at their leisure. Such evidence in trees is a sure sign that leopards are in the area. Dragging a hundred-and-fifty-pound carcass up into a tree is a fantastic feat for an animal who may only weigh a bit more than that himself, but the leopard is all muscle, and can climb trees as easily as most monkeys. He can leap from one branch·to another even while carrying a heavy object in his jaws, and when on the ground he can leap to a height of ten feet or more with almost no apparent effort.

Leopards are considered even more savage than tigers or lions and far more dangerous to a hunter. Some males weigh almost two hundred pounds, while the females are several pounds lighter. The eight-foot length of a big leopard is made up of a stout, muscular body, about fifty-seven inches long, and a slender, furred, and spotted tail of about thirty-nine inches in length. This long tail is usually carried low, but for leaping is used as a balance. It usually has a short dark curl at the very end. Many hunters consider the leopard a lot more intelligent than either lions or tigers, which makes him even more dangerous an adversary.

Leopards feed on deer, goats, sheep, calves, pigs, antelope, monkeys (especially baboons) and occasionally even a human being. Although they normally stick to wild game or domestic animals, their favorite food, strangely enough, is dog. They will go out of their way to stalk one in broad daylight if they spot a careless canine away from home and unaccompanied by man. There have even been reported instances of leopards charging into villages and seizing pet dogs playing with their young owners, leaving the children unhurt. Usually these cats hunt alone, but occasionally a pair will team up and hunt together.

Leopards swim well if need be and are very agile and powerful, making their leaping attack a frightfully effective maneuver, not only from the weight of the animal but by the surprise of the charge. Referring to their method of attack, a group of leopards is known as a "leap," as compared to a "pride" of lions or a "herd" of antelope.

The kittens or cubs are born in the spring, about three months after mating, and they usually number from one to four, rarely five. At birth, the spots on the little tykes are solid, without any yellow center to make them rosettes. Later on, exactly when is not known, the little yellow center begins to appear, and soon they have the "paw-print" rosettes the same as their parents. The family stays together for some months, until the cubs are practically fully grown, when they wander off to lead their own independent lives.

Even such a fierce cat as the leopard produces some mighty cute youngsters, all ears and paws, which make bold, if bumbling, attacks on anything that moves. They roughhouse with each other, chase feathers, stalk their mother's twitching tail tip, and generally behave like any kittens. They do not make good pets, however, and even after months of kindness and good food have been known to turn on their keeper or others who had treated them with kindness, and maul them badly, all in a flash. Just recently a young girl who had helped "tame" six leopards on her father's South African farm was suddenly attacked and mauled by one of her "pets" to the extent of eighty stitches in her head and shoulders. Fortunately, the girl noticed that the eyes of the big cat had suddenly lost their half-closed, sleepy look and had widened—an almost positive sign of attack —so she was somewhat prepared for the rush.

The tracks of the leopard are like those of all cats who do a great deal of living in the trees: rounded and with no trace of the claws showing. The tracks are smaller than those of the lion and measure about three and a half inches in length. When walking, the cat does not place its hind feet in the tracks of the front feet, so that all four feet leave an impression in the dust or mud.

The big cat, like all felines, sharpens its claws on tree trunks and logs and has favorite trees for this purpose, which it visits often to clean and whet its weapons. It also covers with scratched-up dirt any sign it may have to leave in a hunting area, to help conceal its presence.

When leopard tracks are found around or near a native village, terror strikes the hearts of the inhabitants, and usually a mass hunt is organized to drive away or kill the beast. In India, these big cats habitually lurk around such small isolated villages in the hopes of snatching a goat, calf, or, better yet, a dog. During the day, they spend much of their time sleeping in a high tree crotch, or draped over a wide branch concealed by thick foliage. At night they come to life, flex their muscles, and begin to look around for their next meal.

Usually silent stalkers, they give vent occasionally to a wood-sawing cough that quickly stills all other noises in the jungle. This sound, unique with the leopard clan, is one of the most spine-tingling of all nature's noises. Once you have heard it and know what creature makes it, I think you'll agree and understand why all other wild creatures keep very still when spotted *Felis pardus* is looking for dinner nearby.

The leopard has few enemies other than man, who hunts him for his gorgeous coat, often poaching for him in game preserves where he is theoretically safe and protected. The pelt and fur of the leopard are about equal to that of the mink, and rated about 75 per cent of that of the otter in durability. Within the last few years, a booming black market in leopard skins has developed in many parts of the world, resulting in a steady and dangerous loss of these fine big cats. Many agencies are working to encourage the use of other and more plentiful pelts in its place. It would be a shame if these great cats were reduced to a point where they could only be seen in zoos, museums, and in old films, and their carpenter-with-a-dull-saw voice could only be heard on tape and records.

Leopards have a life span of well over twenty years and are often displayed in zoos and circuses. They are rarely trained for animal acts, particularly the black phase, who seems to have a disposition to match his coat. (There is also an albino phase, which is very rare.)

Even big-game hunters with powerful weapons use extreme caution in areas where leopards prowl, and it's just good life insurance when in leopard country to keep an eye on overhead branches where the foliage is thick. It's even better insurance not to walk under them.

Photograph by Leonard Lee Rue III, from National Audubon Society

9. LION
Felis leo

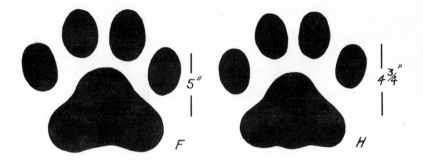

F   5"   H   4¾"

Sometimes you get the impression that you are hearing or reading about several different kinds of lions when you compare the descriptions and comments. In some accounts he is magnificent, vicious, courageous, crafty, and in every tawny inch a real "king of beasts." In others, he is described as a lazy, cowardly, almost stupid critter, who loafs around all day looking noble and regal while his hard-working missis does all the hunting and scrapping and brings up their offspring.

There is a lot of truth in this, for with the cat family, as with the human crowd, there is a great variety of personalities to be found. With all the fact and fiction about lions, there is bound to be a wide difference in opinions as to what he is really like.

All agree on one thing at least: *Felis leo* is quite some cat! Any animal who is from eight to eleven feet long, stands close to four feet high at the shoulder, and which may weigh up to six hundred pounds must be a quite a feline. The lion has figured in literature since the dawn of history from fact to eye-popping fiction, and from the Bible down to comic books. He has been described in legend as a kindly beast with a long memory and affection for a young man who pulled a thorn from its foot, and in fact as a cold-blooded, man-eating killer who held up the building of the Uganda railway by killing twenty-eight laborers in three weeks back in 1898.

He has been the symbol of nations, the emblem of rulers and

colleges, and the mascot of such fighting units as the Lafayette Escadrille and the British Nineteenth Division of World War I fame. Even a blustery March is said to come in or go out like a lion. He has a lot to live up to in many directions.

The lion is a tawny buff all over, with slightly lighter paws and chin. Light spots usually underline his eyes, and his long, stiff whiskers are white. The males develop long manes about their heads, necks, and throats. Often this long hair continues along the sides of the lower body to the hind legs. Young males sport a light colored mane, while those of old males may be dark brown or black. In some areas of their range, the males have very sparse manes and look more like females than the popular image of a masculine lion. The females do not have the heavy mane.

In the wild, the manes of the males are pretty sorry-looking affairs, after snagging brush and bushes, being matted with dirt and blood and burs, and even in spite of grooming by the owner wherever he can reach. Captive lions usually have far more impressive manes than their wild relatives. Young males do not begin to grow manes until they are about three years old.

The cubs are born usually in March or April, although in the hotter parts of their range they have been found at other times of the year. They number from four to six in a litter and arrive in a bed of grass or in thick brush, or even a rocky cave if the mother can find one before the event takes place. They may be born either with eyes open or closed, but even with their eyes open, they seem to have a sort of glassy stare for the first two or three weeks and quite apparently do not see too well for this period. If born with eyes closed, they do not open them for six or seven days.

Cubs are about the size of a house cat when born and for the first few weeks wear thick, woolly coats, which are striped along the body and spotted on the legs. This birthday outfit usually fades out completely after about six months, but occasionally a two-or-three-year-old cub may be found still wearing traces of this spotted and stripped outfit, like a favorite blanket he hates to give up.

Lion cubs are playful, and when brought up in captivity with good care and kindness become quite tame, though hard on the furniture and even the owners. Playing with a cat weighing a few hundred pounds can be pretty rough even if it's all in good fun.

Originally the lion was found over much of Europe (some say all over the world, for that matter) but was exterminated during the Roman Empire. Lions are no longer found in Europe, Turkey, Arabia, and probably there are none in Persia. Even in India, where one man alone once killed four hundred in a few years, they have been eliminated except in one or two small areas. In Africa they were exterminated except for those in the southern portions, and even now they are only found in numbers in Kruger Park and other national wildlife preserves in southern Africa. What a shame to eliminate such a majestic cat, even a dangerous one!

There are many interesting characteristics about the so-called king of beasts. For one thing, he is usually frightened by small children or such domestic items as a flapping laundry line, and he won't even approach a small animal called a zorille (a little south African creature resembling a skunk).

Another interesting and baffing point of interest, literally, is the "horn," or "stinger," as some natives call it, hidden in the bushy black tassel on the end of the male's tail. This small horny scale or bony scrap of material is attached to the skin at the very tip of the vertebra, and no one seems to know how, or even if, his ancestors ever used this, and, if so, for what purpose.

Perhaps the most talked-about talent of the lion is his roar, and deservedly so, for it is one of the most nerve-shattering of all of nature's noises, even when you are familiar with it. Some keepers at zoos have told me that no matter how often they hear it, it still gives them a shudder, and even with the cat behind stout bars, they have caught themselves retreating over the guard rail when Leo cuts loose with a blast behind them. I've felt the same impulse many times.

The noise is terrific, and the animal usually holds his head close to the ground when really wishing to impress the countryside. This seems to give the noise even more volume, and he needs no loud-speaker to reach an audience a mile away. His voice also includes grunting coughs, snarls, and assorted rumblings, all apparently with a special purpose and for a specific circumstance or mood. The lioness is not quite as vocal as the male but can, like most gals, hold up her end of a conversation if need be.

The great strength and agility of the lion, as big as he is, is almost unbelievable. He can run a hundred yards at almost a mile a minute, leap a twelve-foot fence or over a ten-foot thorn fence, even when carrying something in his mouth. On level ground he can leap over twenty feet, and some reports say leaps of over thirty feet with a bit of a running start. A big lion can break the neck of a zebra with one blow. He can down a larger animal with one paw on the shoulder and another on the nose for leverage, and then drag it for several yards to where he wishes to consume it as easily as you would tote a bag of groceries.

The female does much of the hunting, with the male joining her after she has done the marketing. He covers what he does not eat with brush and comes back later on for further meals, sometimes staying nearby until even the spoiled meat has been consumed.

Lions will eat almost anything they can catch, large or small, from cane rats and bush pigs to zebras and larger game. They hunt in open country where game is plentiful and usually do this from the ground, after a stalk followed by a fast charge at great speed and a crashing attack. Young lions climb trees very well until they are about half grown, and even a full-grown lion will sometimes nap in the low branches of a sturdy tree, sprawled out on a stout branch with his legs dangling down on both sides, like a small boy.

These big cats are quite sociable, often traveling in good-sized groups, consisting of cubs, half-grown lions, and adults, even some old cats hardly able to hunt for themselves and content to mooch the leavings after the rest have finished. Such parties or family groups are called "prides," and may number as many as two dozen lions, of all sizes and ages, in one gang. When two such groups meet at a watering hole, they seldom engage in really serious scraps, although they may indulge in some pretty hair-raising roaring contests before settling down to share the water. Occasionally one adventurous cat will approach another from the other group, and a short, vicious battle will occur, but usually only during the mating season will the males engage in a serious combat with another of their species. Scraps over meals and between the ladies do not really count as grade-A lion fights, although they can be noisy affairs, with plenty of dust and occasional flying fur.

Lions may pair for a year or more, keeping together as a family unit until the youngsters are old enough to go off on their own and find romance for themselves. Lions are in the prime of their life at about five or six years, although they often live for as long as thirty years in captivity, if their health is kept up. Most animals in big zoos are well fed, cared for like the valuable animals they are, and are actually far better off than on their own in the wilds.

Interestingly enough, lions can be bred with tigers, and the resulting cubs are called either "tiglons" (some call them "tigons") or "ligers," depending upon which animal is the father. If a male lion is bred with a female tiger, the cubs are ligers, and if the father is a tiger, the youngsters are tiglons or tigons.

The tracks of lions are found near water holes or usually near big herds of game animals upon which the cats feed. Like all cats, the lion has five toes on the front feet and four on the hind feet, but only four toes register on all four pads, along with the palm and heel pads. Some tracks seem to reveal that the palm pad has three lobes on the posterior edge while others appear to have only two. Here again, as in the case of most animals, there is really no typical track without any variation at all. The lion is a silent stalker and so usually places his hind feet in the tracks of the front feet when hunting for his meals. An adult lion's tracks measure around five inches in length, with some even larger. The claws do not register except when fighting or perhaps when the tracks are found where he has made a kill. The best place to find them is around a water hole.

This great cat, long told about in history, poem and song, and so magnificently portrayed in murals, paintings, and sculpture, has played such a big part in so many symbolic ways that it would be unthinkable to have him vanish from the globe. The "Simba" of Africa, whether or not actually the king he has been claimed to be in legend and song, deserves a perpetual place, if not a throne, in wildlifes future. I'm sure he'll always be perched there, looking every inch the part of "king of the cats" in spite of fact or fiction.

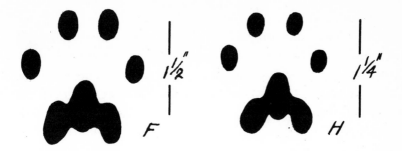

F $1\frac{1}{2}''$

H $1\frac{1}{4}''$

10. MARGAY
Felis wiedii

The ocelot has quite a few relatives, some larger and some smaller, and one of the most interesting is his smaller kinsman the margay, found in the vast forests of Central and South America. It is also known as the "tiger cat," as are many of these related spotted and striped cats of the jungle.

Frequently seen in zoos, this small feline is often confused with the ordinary big house cat of the "tiger cat" variety, for the head is quite house-cat-like. The photo of the margay is of a young one so the ears appear to be quite big, giving it a sort of a pleasant "kitty" look. As a matter of fact, the natives of the areas in which this little cat is found often catch them when young and sell them to tourists who visit these countries.

As youngsters they do make fine pets, affectionate and very playful, as well as colorful, but their wild nature begins to come out as they mature, and by the time they are fully grown they are usually far better off in a zoo. Their affectionate nature may

Photograph by John H. Gerard, from National Audubon Society

76

suddenly change, and their owner may find he has a savage animal in his home almost over night, in spite of good care, plenty of food, and kindness.

Although more spotted than striped, the margay has a long, barred tail, like many of his relatives. The head is rounded, and the fur quite coarse and of a dull, grizzled color, lighter below. The nose is pinkish, and the long whiskers are white. The lips, chin, and throat are creamy white, and there are two dark stripes running up over the head from the inner corners of the eyes like war paint on an Indian. The cheeks also are decorated with white areas, dark lines, and color patches. The whiskers grow from black dots arranged in rows along the upper lips.

The ears are quite rounded, and in the youngsters seem all out of proportion to the rest of his body. They are light inside and rimmed with dark on the back surfaces.

The body of the margay measures about two feet in length, with a foot and a half of tail behind it. The animal stands about a foot high and weighs between fifteen and twenty pounds. The paws are small, and the entire cat, when mature, is built for agility and speed in the trees.

The margay is extremely agile in hunting for food in the branches of the forest where it lives. It spends most of its waking hours hunting in the trees for birds, lizards, small arboreal animals and an occasional snake. It does hunt upon the ground as well, but prefers to hunt aloft for its own safety. Its fine night sight and surefootedness enables it to race through the branches after its prey with astonishing sureness and speed.

This great agility and speed, whether aloft or below, is one of the best life insurance policies it has, enabling it to escape attack from the jaguar and other larger cats, who in turn live upon the margay, or would like to.

Not too much is known about its wild habits, but the youngsters, ranging from one to three in a litter, although generally twins, are born in a hollow log or tree, the latter being much preferred if a suitable one can be found. The baby cats arrive at almost any season of the year, as with most tropical cats, and are fed by the mother until they are able to go with her and begin to hunt for themselves. Even as kittens they are very active, brawling with each other and doing "battle" with anything they can find.

They nurse for several weeks and then begin to gnaw at bones or worry bits of more mature food brought home by the mother, finally learning to hunt for game by themselves. Once they learn to climb well and have gained strength, they are taken on night hunting trips and taught the business of survival. At about a year they are really on their own, selecting their own territory and ready for mating.

The tracks of the margay show tiny toe pads, and the track is about the size of that of an ordinary house cat. The front feet are slightly larger than the hind feet, as in the case of most cats. The tiny claws are needle-sharp and kept that way by scratching on a branch or tree trunk or post at frequent intervals. Sometimes as a margay rests on a branch it will work its claws in and out of their pockets and dig them into the bark of the tree to keep them strong and clean.

Like all cats, the margay cleans its coat with its tongue, and the mother keeps her kittens well groomed from the time of their birth. They also groom their whiskers and paws after eating, like the domestic cats we are so familiar with. The margay's whiskers, like those of its huge relative, the tiger, are dark at the roots, turning white further from the lip, and quite stiff, so that their owner can use them to judge the size of openings it must pass through.

Typically catlike, the margay is a pretty silent chap, using his voice only occasionally: when angered, fighting, or in a particularly romantic frame of mind. Then it consists of yowls and meows very much like any city tomcat on a back fence. At other times it may snarl in anger at a missed dinner, or give out with hisses and spits when confronted with another margay to dispute its territory.

This little tropical and semitropical cat is found from Mexico to Peru, spending its days napping on a cool branch or shady thicket resting place or dozing in its hollow tree or log, and racing through the branches at night after an elusive meal. It's a small but interesting member of the cat family, and the next time you visit a zoo see if you can find one.

Photograph by Hugh M. Halliday, from National Audubon Society

F   3"   H   2¾"

11. MOUNTAIN LION
Felis cougar

This member of the cat family, if nothing else, is the most "named" of all of them, and I even hesitate to call him the mountain lion, and the *Felis cougar*. Some zoologists list him as the cougar *(Felis cougar)*, some as the puma *(Felis concolor)*, some as American panther *(Felis hippolestes,* which means horse-killer), and so on. Other names he is known by include: panther, painter, catamount, brown tiger, sneak cat, red tiger, silver lion, deer killer, indian devil, screamer, varmint, king cat, big cat, etc. There is almost no end to the list, but it's all the same old critter underneath.

Aside from the jaguar, occasionally found in the United States, this is our largest cat. Its range was originally over most of the first forty-eight states, but it is now limited to the western and wildest parts of the country from Vancouver to the Gulf, with some in Florida and an occasional one being reported as seen or tracked in the wildest portions of New England, New York, and Pennsylvania. No photographic or physical proof has been produced of the animal's actually being in the latter states for some years, but the fact remains that there are plenty of wild regions in these areas where these cats might still be living, far from man and his cameras.

They prefer the wildest possible areas, and as they are shy and difficult to see under the best of conditions, it is possible they are still about in areas where they have been thought to be extinct. I have a faded photo taken in 1881 which shows a mountain lion shot in Barnard, Vermont, by a Mr. Alexander Crowell. This lion weighed 182½ pounds and was seven feet long. It was killed with a percussion-cap doubled-barreled shotgun.

There are also occasional reports of sightings in Nova Scotia, New Brunswick, and in the southern Appalachian wilderness. It may be futile and wishful thinking, but I for one hope there is some truth to the rumors that this great cat is still living in the eastern part of the United States, where he was once unquestionably the "king of the forest."

The cat averages about seven and a half feet long, with some males reaching nine feet in length, including a three-foot tail. They stand about twenty-five inches high at the shoulder and weigh up to about 210 pounds, with the average about 150 pounds. Females are slightly smaller and lighter.

The head is small and round, and the ears are held erect unless fighting or angry, when they are held back close to the head. The color varies with the region in which they are found but is generally a tawny brown or buckskin above and creamy white below, including the throat and chin. The front of the upper lips is white, with black patches between lips and cheeks. Whiskers are white, and the inside of the ears are white as well, while the outer back edges are black. The nose is pinkish, and the eyes yellow. The tip of the heavy tail is also dark brown to black. The fur is short, close to the body, and kept well groomed.

In contrast to the adults, the cubs are born with tawny coats spotted with black, and with striped tails, banded with dark brown or black. This off-beat infant outfit is probably some evolutionary reversion to a remote ancestor who lived in the jungle and needed such protection. The spotted coat, along with that of the young of the white-tailed deer of the East Coast, may just be nature's way of added protection for the kittens until they can get along without it. At any rate, this dappled and striped coat begins to fade after two months and it is lost entirely after six months.

The color of the adults varies with where they live. Those living in the jungles of South America and Central America (where this cat is also found), are darker than those found in arid desert country, where the coat is a much lighter and grayer shade to match the background against which it must hunt to survive.

A pair, once mated, will stay together until the arrival of the cubs, when the mother usually drives the father away. Cubs may number from one to five, but two or three is the usual number. Born blind, they open their eyes in nine to fourteen days, begin to crawl around after about seven weeks, and are usually weaned at three months. They may stay with the mother for as long as two years, but generally drift away after about a year to start their own families.

The life expectancy, barring accident, may be as long as twenty years, although some claim the females die much earlier. The males generally live alone except during the mating season, although some naturalists say both parents take care of the cubs. Others say the female drives the male away when the cubs arrive, as I mentioned. Here again, the animal is the subject for argument.

One thing is sure: mountain lions have a terrific appetite, and must have a great deal of fresh meat to keep in good health. Their favorite way of hunting is to pounce upon their prey from an overhanging ledge or branch. They usually kill by breaking the neck of the animal they leap upon. They feed upon deer, sheep, horses and cattle, as well as small animals in the north, and in the tropics they eat tapirs, agoutis, peccaries (small wild pigs), sloths, and several other tropical animals, even birds when they can catch them. In the north, and when they can find them, they enjoy a chicken dinner as well as any of us.

If they cannot finish a meal, they drag it into a safe place and cover it with brush to conceal it. They do not drag it up into trees, as does the leopard, nor do they eat carrion, so they will stay with a kill only until it begins to spoil. A strong male can drag a nine-hundred-pound animal for many feet to a place where it can be concealed. Mountain lions require about eighty pounds of meat for a meal, so they spend almost all of their waking time hunting.

The hunting range of a mountain lion may be fifty miles across, and the cat covers probably twenty miles a night in search of game. In this territory, he usually has favorite ledges or limbs over game trails, near watering places, or where he has made earlier kills, which he visits frequently. He will also have favorite trees or stumps where he scratches to sharpen his claws. Mountain lions like thick cover, not only because that is where game is found, but also as a concealment for themselves. The dens are usually high in the rocky ledges where man is seldom seen.

These cats are excellent climbers, and when hunted with dogs they will take to a tree when the pups get too close to their padded heels. Once treed, they will usually stay there, awaiting the end, but occasionally they will leap over the heads of the dogs and escape before the hunter arrives. A treed lion seems to lose all courage and unfortunately often is killed when he could have escaped with a bit more courage and resourcefulness.

About the only other enemy besides man that a mountain lion has is an occasional big bear, a jaguar (in the tropics), or the lowly porcupine. In a fair fight between a jaguar and this mountain cat it is said that the jaguar will be whipped by the lighter mountain lion. That would be a real cat fight, worth watching—but from a good, safe distance!

This interesting cat has a north-south range not equaled by any other American animal, for it apparently can adapt itself to cold mountaintops or steaming jungles with equal ease. In the north, it thrives on wild and chilly peaks, and in Florida it does just fine in the humid swamplands, while in the jungles of South America it does equally well. The mountain lions of the hot areas are smaller than those of the colder portions of its vast range, but they are also more aggressive by nature.

Regardless of where captured, this cat makes a good zoo animal, good-natured, quiet, and an interesting animal to display. If caught very young, mountain lions even make affectionate captives and become quite tame, permitting their keepers to scratch them while they purr most contentedly, like some overgrown tabby cat.

One outstanding characteristic of this big cat is its voice. It has become legendary, and no wonder, for it has a whole denful of calls, growls, wails, screams, and screeches, enough to scare the daylights out of anyone. Unless hunting as silently as all cats, the animal is quite apt to express itself vocally. It purrs when contented, growls over its food, and snarls when annoyed or frustrated, but its vocalizing during the mating season is tops for wildness.

85

The screams of this cat have been described as a person being tortured, a woman in mortal agony, and the shrieks of a lost soul—any of which would be enough to make a person poke up his campfire and wish he were somewhere else. The sound of this cat has become traditional as a means of adding excitement to almost any movie or western thriller, and just the mention of a mountain lion in a script is guaranteed to make the audience shudder.

As a matter of fact, the animal is extremely shy and wary when it comes to man and his scent. In spite of all the accounts of its attacking man, stalking lost children, and carrying off infants, such tales are invariably pure fiction. It is possible that in very isolated instances a mountain lion has attacked a human being when cornered or surprised, or that a wounded, sick, or very old animal unable to catch its normal prey has killed a child wandering alone in the wilds, but generally speaking this big cat, in spite of its size and power, is the greatest coward of all the big cats when it faces man—even a small one.

Like all cats, it may be curious and follow a human at a distance, and as a matter of fact I believe I was followed by one of these big tabbies as a small boy in New Hampshire. It was late one winter afternoon, and I'd gone deep into the woods to cut a Christmas tree. The snow was crusted heavily, almost enough to bear my weight, and coming back at twilight something followed me until I could see the lights of the town below me in the valley. I could hear its crunching through the crust behind me in the spruces when I stopped to rest.

Deer will not travel when the crust is heavy, for it cuts their slender legs, bear had long been asleep for the winter, and neither a bobcat nor a lynx could have broken the crust, as this "follower" did so easily. Had I not been concerned over the growing darkness, or had I had something with me besides a single-shot .22 rifle and about three cartridges, I might have waited for whatever it was to come closer, but let's face it squarely—I was scared to death and couldn't get back to town fast enough. That night it snowed heavily, so I did not go back by daylight to look for tracks. I'll never know what it was that did follow me, but some of the old local hunters I talked with were sure it was one of these big, curious cats. I like to think so, too.

The tracks of the mountain lion are typically catlike in shape and pad arrangement. They measure about three and three-quarter inches long, and the marks of the front feet are larger than those of the hind feet. These cats do not step exactly in their own tracks, and so you will often find the imprints of all four feet instead of the row of "single" prints apparently left by other cats. On level ground this animal can leap twenty feet without apparent effort, and when pursued it can cover thirty feet almost as easily. It is an amazingly agile animal.

The mountain lion is a very neat animal, grooming itself repeatedly, and has the commendable habit of using a specific place as a toilet, scraping dirt over any droppings after use. These are called "scratchings" or "sign heaps," and sooner or later they attract a mate into the area and an eventual meeting takes place. These big cats bear kittens every two or three years and take fine care of them, keeping them clean and groomed, as well as keeping their den free from any great amount of rubbish and refuse. Altogether they are really fine housekeepers and family-type creatures.

In spite of his attacks on domestic livestock when other food is hard to get, his bad reputation on the movie and TV screens, and his unearthly voice when in a romantic or frustrated mood, he's a pretty decent sort of citizen. Let's hope that for many years to come he'll still be around to dress up our western landscape and perhaps follow small boys home in the twilight.

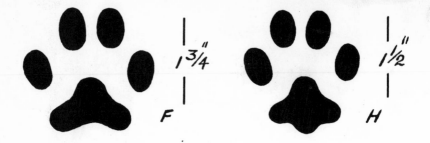

F $1\tfrac{3}{4}''$ $1\tfrac{1}{2}''$ H

12. OCELOT
Felis pardalis

One of the few wild cats which can be made into a quite affectionate, if demanding, pet is the ocelot, a sleek, colorful, and trim little chap that ranges from the southern United States down into Patagonia. According to some, there is evidence that the ocelot once roamed as far north in the United States as Ohio. This small wild cat is also known as the "tiger cat," "leopard cat," and "little jaguar."

The ocelot is a sort of miniature jaguar as far as coloring goes, with a crazy collection of spots, rosettes, and stripes on its lithe and agile body. Some are four feet long, with a fifteen-inch tail. Females are about ten inches shorter. They stand about fifteen inches high at the shoulder and have quite large, black-edged ears. Their weight runs between twenty-five and thirty-five pounds. Their coat is basically a tawny yellow beneath the black spots, with the throat and under parts creamy white and also spotted. Interestingly enough, the two sides of an ocelot's

coat never match in pattern. Some species are almost gray in background color but have the same wild assortment of darker spots and stripes.

Along the neck of the animal, and in some cases along the sides, the spots run together into stripes, and the tail is decorated with wide bars rather than spots. The tail, contrary to many so marked cats, has a white tip instead of the usual black one.

The inside of the legs and paws is light in color, but still spotted, and the paws are covered with small dots. The fur is short but thick, and the legs are stout. The neck is short, and the head is small and truly catlike; the face is marked with contrasting bands of the basic color, white, and black. The whiskers are long and white, and occasionally one or two will grow out of the cat's cheeks as well as from its lips. The upper lips are marked with rows of black dots from which the whiskers grow, although not every dot sprouts one of these sensing organs.

Ocelots are quite easily tamed (if caught very young or born in captivity) and are about the size of the jaguarundi, or roughly one and a half to twice the size of the ordinary house cat. Their eyes are rather unusual in that they appear to be all iris, with no whites at all. They are reddish brown, and the cats' night sight is most keen, enabling them to get about and hunt with great efficiency. No cat can see in total darkness, but it can get about with a minimum of light from the moon or stars and do so very well.

In the tropical forests, where they are found in greatest abundance, ocelots hunt for food not only on the ground but in the trees. They are agile and sure-footed climbers and often dine on sleeping monkeys who feel perfectly safe high in the branches of tall trees. They sometimes play "dead" to lure monkeys within range of their lightning fast paws. They also hunt and eat a variety of small mammals: rats, mice, birds, snakes, and other reptiles, some of which they hunt in the daytime. By keeping to the sunlit shadows where their coats blend with the patterns of sunlight and shadow, they are almost invisible and can hunt with great success even in daylight.

The fur of the ocelot is short and soft but not particularly thick. It may vary in thickness with individual animals, which may be the result of diet or weather where they live.

During much of the daytime, the ocelot sleeps or naps in some secluded thicket where he hopes he is safe from harm, or perhaps lies stretched out on a broad limb in a shady grove. As twilight approaches, he comes to life, stretches to flex his firm muscles, grooms himself a bit, and then starts out looking for a bite to eat. One reason zoo visitors are frequently disappointed in the activity of these cats is that they are nocturnal animals and have always spent the bright hours asleep. Some who have been born and brought up in captivity seem to have adjusted to the new life, as they are regularly fed during the day, instead of at night as they would be in the wild state, and so move about their enclosures during the day. Even so, you will often find them napping on a shelf at the back of the cage, or dozing on a man-provided tree trunk.

An adult ocelot requires about five pounds of meat a day, and in the wild, an adult ocelot will turn to such larger game as young goats, pigs and lambs to satisfy its hunger. In our own Texas and Arizona and New Mexico, ocelots occasionally develop a great passion for poultry—much to the frustration of the farmers. When hunting, a pair of these sleek cats will often team up to corner their quarry, keeping in touch with each other with low mewing sounds.

Ocelots apparently are equally at home either in dense jungles or in the open country, adjusting their hunting techniques to whatever the surroundings and circumstances. The majority of them live in dense forests and are seldom seen in the wild state by man. The mating season is usually in June or July in the cool climes of the southern hemisphere.

The kittens, usually twins, are born at almost any time of the year in the tropics and during the fall in the cooler climates. The kittens are blind at birth and arrive in a rocky den or hollow log lined with soft grasses and other suitable materials. They are soon able to stagger around the den, and after they are weaned and gain in strength, they are taught to stalk and kill by their mother.

The tracks of the ocelot are about the size of a bobcat's, measuring about one and a half inches in length. The hind paws are as usual, a bit smaller. The ocelot's trail will wander around the forest floor, ending now and then at the foot of a tree it has climbed looking for a meal. Examination of the bark of such trees will often reveal small scratches from its claws or light hair from the belly or legs of the cat as it climbs. Tracks are found near water, where they may go to drink; on dusty game trails; or at the base of favorite roosting trees of birds or monkeys.

The voice of the ocelot is similar to that of any of the smaller cats—a collection of snarls, soft mewing noises when hunting in pairs after dark, and tomcattish yowls during the mating season. Usually the ocelot is a silent stalker and pads about the forest like a shadow dressed in a mottled coat.

A tidy animal, the ocelot keeps its coat and den neat and clean, and like the mountain lion, it has the very commendable habit of selecting a certain spot as a toilet, using it repeatedly and covering up any droppings by pawing dirt over the spot. It keeps its youngsters well washed and groomed, licks its paws after eating, and cleans its whiskers as well.

Ocelots will not attack a man, but, like any cat, will fight savagely when attacked or cornered. When attacking game too large to kill at once, they seize it by the neck and hold it to the ground until it expires. Small game can usually only escape the attack of an ocelot by getting into a refuge too small for the larger animal to follow, or too well protected for the cat to dig open. Since cats, unlike dogs, are not good diggers, this has saved many a small creature's life when fleeing from this fancy feline of the jungle.

Photograph by A. W. Ambler, from National Audubon Society

13. PALLAS CAT
Felis manul

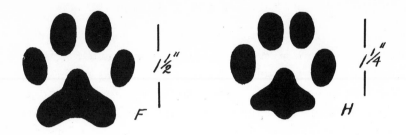

Undoubtedly, all of our domestic long-haired cats are descended from this most interesting wild cat found in central Asia from Transcaspia to Kansu and Mongolia and southward to Iran, Afghanistan, and Tibet.

The Pallas cat has several most unique characteristics for a cat. His ears, unlike those of most cats, are set very wide apart on his head and are short and rounded instead of pointed. His tail is very bushy, almost ending in a ball, more like that of a fox, and it is half as long as his body.

His total length is from twenty-seven to thirty seven-inches, and he appears quite solidly built and heavy due to his extremely heavy fur coat. This coat is particularly long and thick on the throat and belly, so that when he lies down to sleep, or crouches in wait for a meal, his body is insulated from the cold ground beneath him. He lives in areas where the cold and wet are with him all year round, where even the summer nights can be very cold, and where winter nights are always extremely cold and windy. The heavy fur coat protects him very well when walking through, or sleeping in, deep snow.

Living as he does where there is much ice and snow and little natural cover, the fact that his ears are set low enables him to peer over any slight bit of cover without revealing his presence to a possible dinner a few feet away. This, too, is another of nature's ways of making it possible for him to survive.

PALLAS CAT—*Felis manul*

The coat of the Pallas cat is pale buff tinged with a reddish brown, and with a faint sprinkling of black hairs. It is very thick, almost like wool, with a heavy undercoat of fine warm hair. His bushy tail has several faint rings about it, and the whole tip is black. There is occasionally the faint suggestion of dark bars across the back of this cat, and the face and head are patterned with light and dark bars and spots. The whiskers are long and white, and the upper lips and chin as well as the throat and belly are somewhat lighter than the rest of the animal. In summer the coat sheds, and the cat appears thinner, but when the cold months come again he promptly grows his usual long underwear to be ready for the freezing weather ahead.

The Pallas cat preys upon such small animals as chipmunks and the jumping jerboas in the warmer countries. Where the snows and ice are too much for these small mammals, he dines on pikas and other rock- and snow-country mammals and birds.

Unfortunately, the Mongols who live where the Pallas cat is found are not interested in the home life and domestic problems of the local wild cats, so very little information about them can be gathered. It is assumed that the kittens appear in the warmer months and number from one to four, as with similar-sized cats. Their den is probably among the sheltered rocks on the sunny side of the mountain, where the youngsters will have an opportunity to warm themselves when the sun is out. They may be born blind, like most cats, but no information on this is available. There is still much in nature to keep naturalists busy for a long time to come.

The voice of the Pallas cat consists of the usual catlike noises, but it is reported that the meow of this odd cat is so abrupt that it sounds almost like the yap of a small dog. Others who have heard it say it more nearly resembles the hoot of a small owl.

95

In the winter, the tracks made by this cat resemble those of a small lynx, due to the heavy fur around the toes. During the summer months this fur is not as prominent, and the tracks appear smaller. But in snow the tracks appear much larger than the paw pads really are, and a good-sized Pallas cat will leave a track about two inches across. The hind feet leave a slightly smaller track.

Few zoos have ever been fortunate enough to exhibit one of these odd-looking cats, but those that have been put upon display have adapted well to captivity, being docile and easy to get along with, even if not really tame or affectionate. This is most unusual and fascinating member of the cat family from far-off Asia and the snow and ice of her vast mountains.

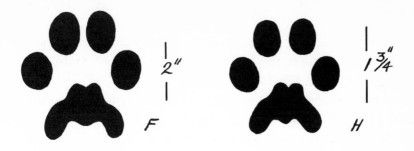

14. SERVAL
Felis serval

This comparatively small wild cat from Africa appears to be assembled from spare parts left over from other cats. Contrary to most cats, he is neither streamlined nor slinky-looking. His tail is too short for a long-tailed cat and much to long for a bobtailed cat. His legs, on the other hand, are too long for his body, and the front ones seem much longer than the hind ones. His neck is also too long; his ears are tall and pointed and sit high on his head and close together. Outside of this he's a handsome chap.

His coat is a reddish buff or a reddish orange, sprinkled with dark-brown or black spots and streaks. The nose is flesh-colored and quite big. His face is sprinkled with small dots, and his lips, chin, and under parts are lighter in color, with a sprinkling of black blotches and spots. His odd-length tail has dark bars on top but is light underneath, and no particular pattern seems to have been followed when designing his coat markings, for one leg may be striped and another spotted on the same cat.

Photograph by New York Zoological Society

The serval has white hairs on the inside of his ears, but the outside is marked with spots and bars of dark color. He does not have the rosettes of some species of cats, but usually carries just spots and short bars, against the buff color above and the creamy white below. There is occasionally a black phase, in which the spots are faintly visible.

SERVAL — *Felis serval*

A big serval will stand from eighteen to twenty-five inches high at the shoulder and weigh from fifteen to about twenty-five pounds. His length will be about forty-four inches, including a foot of tail.

The natives of South Africa call him the "bush cat," for he prefers the thick brush country to the open plains. His range is from the Cape of Good Hope north to Algeria, and he is found in practically every part of the continent where food is plentiful and he can find thick brush for concealment.

The natives hunt him with dogs that force him to climb trees, where he is easily killed or shaken out of the branches for the dogs to finish off. He is not a vicious or ferocious fighter and can be tamed to some extent if caught quite young, but he does not thrive in captivity. The serval needs exercise to maintain good health even if well fed, and while captive will refuse to exercise enough to maintain good health and vigor. Kittens raised in captivity are never really tame and have to be watched.

The silent stalk and a sudden fast, rushing charge for the last few feet make up this cat's hunting technique. His long legs enable him to cover the ground at a high rate of speed for at least a few yards. He can also make astonishing leaps for a small cat, easily catching birds perched in apparent safety as much as ten feet above the ground. If they are perched higher, he will climb within leaping range with ease and agility.

Birds of all kinds, mice, rats, various types of hares, and even some small antelope and the young of larger game are the serval's food. He knows his hunting limitations quite well and usually stalks his prey until only a short rush is required to secure it. Near native villages he develops a taste for poultry and often raids chicken houses or attacks them when roosting in branches of trees or rafters of outbuildings.

Like all cats, he hates to dig, so the female usually moves

99

into any unoccupied den she can find for her housekeeping and the delivery of her youngsters. The male is relegated to sleep elsewhere and usually selects a dark thicket or small cave nearby and close to water if possible.

The serval prefers long grass and reeds and low brush as cover for his den and hunting, and although he is usually found near water and can swim if necessary, he never seeks escape in that direction, preferring to climb a tree, where he is usually trapped.

Not much is known of the family life of the serval, except that the kittens may arrive at almost any time of the year, and that they number from one to four in a litter. Probably, like all young members of the cat family, they are born blind and nurse for the first few weeks of their life, opening their eyes after about ten days. At about six weeks they are weaned, when they begin to try out more substantial foodstuffs. In the kitten stage, some are almost black in color, some are brown with a dark streak down their backs, and some are quite light, with the darker back stripe. I've examined such a litter of three in study skins from the Belgian Congo, so apparently it can be composed of quite an assortment of color phases, at least in the kittens. These change their coats as they mature and probably take on the spots and bars of their parents after about six months.

The track of this oddly designed cat is about two inches long with quite rounded, rather than elongated, paw toe pads. The whole paw track is quite round. When walking, this cat has a sort of widespread track, with the feet apart rather than in a straight line as in the case of many cats. The serval can travel swiftly when need be but usually wanders about looking for game signs or peering up into the branches of trees for roosting birds.

The voice of the serval is a collection of cat noises, hisses, growls, snarls, and spitting noises. He is, of course, a silent stalker, like all cats, and only gives vent to his feelings when fighting, defending his food, or during the mating season when he is as vocal as most cats looking for a mate.

Thanks to a not-too-attractive coat of little interest to furriers, a liking for thick brush and the back country, this oddly constructed member of the Felidae family will probably be with us for as long as cats exist.

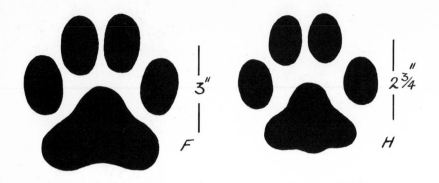

F 3"

H 2¾"

15. SNOW LEOPARD
Felis uncia

The most beautiful of all leopards, according to many, is the great snow leopard, or ounce, found in the high Himalayas of Asia. This elusive cat ranges from the Himalayas to the Altai Mountains of Mongolia and is found at altitudes well above ten thousand feet. In many instances he has been reported as high as eighteen thousand feet during the summer months in this cold and forbidding part of the world. In the freezing winter months, he descends to around six thousand feet or lower for food, but is almost never found below this altitude—a strange habitat indeed for a member of the leopard clan.

This unusual animal, a complete about-face from the leopard of the tropical jungles of Africa and Asia, prefers the cold and ice, but in spite of his great fur coat can adjust quite easily to warmer climes if sufficient shade is provided. The Bronx Zoo (New York Zoological Park) has two of these rare leopards on

Photograph by New York Zoological Society

display, and while they spend much of their time in the shade of their dens, they do appear outside at feeding time, where they may be deservedly admired.

Their coats are exceptionally long and thick and of a yellowish-gray color with black spots in vivid contrast. The tail is really a thing of feline beauty, heavy and barred with rosettes and with a jet-black tip. The under side of the animal, throat, and lips are white but still blotched with rosettes and spots. The feet are big and well furred between the toes for better protection when walking on ice and snow.

One would think that such an animal would be most conspicuous in a land of ice and snow, but there are enough rocks and bare spots, where small game live, for the ounce to find good cover for his camouflage hunting jacket. His eyes are a smoky blue-gray, perhaps the better to conceal himself, and, according to native legend, he drags his heavy tail behind him to wipe away his footprints in the snow. This may be true, but if it does destroy his tracks, it's just by accident; however, this makes a fine tale to tell.

The head and face of the ounce are spotted with little dots and spots, but the chest, belly, and throat are usually unmarked. The inside of the legs is creamy white or white, and the dark spots frequently run around into this area from the outside of the legs.

The snow leopard has fine sharp, retractile claws, like almost all other members of the Felidae family, but it is doubtful that he can climb trees well, if at all. As there are no trees worth climbing where he lives, he may never have had this experience. He hunts his food upon the ground, living on small rodents, wild sheep, goats, and, when other food is hard to find, even the wild ponies of the natives.

The kittens, usually three or four in number, are born about three months after mating, and they arrive in a snug den high in the rocky peaks, away from man and his tracks. Not much is known about their rearing, weaning, and training, for they are born where man seldom goes. It is assumed that they are born during the warmer months of the year.

The snow leopard is about seven feet long, but some of them reach an even greater length. The tail is three feet or more in length. (One skin I measured had a forty-eight inch body and a thirty-two inch tail.) The male animal weighs from seventy-five to a hundred pounds, and the females are a few pounds lighter. The thick fur makes them appear much heavier, but in reality their bodies are a great deal lighter than those of the regular leopard, which may reach two hundred pounds in weight.

During the summer, at least in captivity, the snow leopard sheds great snarls and blobs of fur as the heavy coat thins out for the warmer months, but when the cold weather is due again, the big cat grows another heavy coat to be ready for it. This includes long and heavier hair on the feet and between the toe pads, which will alter the size and shape of the tracks of the animal.

The paw prints of the cat are almost as big as those of the large leopards of Africa and Asia, and they measure from about two and a half inches in length up to a bit over three inches. Those of females are a bit smaller, in proportion with their size. In both sexes the hind feet leave a slightly smaller print than the front feet. I measured many skins of these big cats, and looked as closely as possible at the feet of snow leopards sleeping on their sides just inside the bars of their enclosures. (I've often wondered which of us would have been the most surprised had they suddenly waked up to find me staring at their feet, sketch pad in hand?)

On a hard surface, the tracks would be of the size I indicate above, but in deep snow they would appear nearly twice that size, for the cat's furry feet make quite a hole in the snow. The trail would wander considerably as the cat hunted here and there for food, near ledges, small caves, ravines, and near whatever watering places could be found.

The snow leopard can, of course, like all cats, leap several feet when in a hurry to attack or escape, and some say he can leap upwards for as much as ten feet to a ledge or cave entrance. He certainly has no trouble attaining a high shelf in his cage.

In captivity these big cats show how much disposition can vary with different animals of the same species. Some are quiet and even gentle, making friends with their keeper. Others are moody, temperamental, and always savage. However, they all have one thing in common: their love of romping in the snow during the winter months when it drifts into their cages.

Some snow leopards seem to thrive in captivity, living for ten years or more and giving birth to cubs. In the wild the animal may live even longer, for the wild tropical leopard is known to live for over twenty years, and, barring starvation or accident, the snow leopard might do even better.

The voice of the *felis uncia* is a weird combination of growls, snarls, and coughs, much like that of other leopards. I've recorded the cough of the snow leopard on my tape recorder, and it does sound like someone sawing wood. This is not a particularly frightening sound unless you know what it is—but once you have heard it you'll never forget it.

Unlike the leopards of the tropics, the snow leopard has to hunt on the ground among the rocks and ledges, or by leaping upon his prey from a ledge above. In spite of this un-leopard-like technique, without a tree in sight, this big snow-country cat makes a pretty good living just the same. Nature is marvelously clever at adapting her creatures to whatever situation or conditions they find themselves in.

The fact that this big cat does live in inaccessible places gives him the great advantage of not being too much bothered by animal trappers and hunters. This makes him one of the rarest animals to be exhibited to the public in zoos or circuses. The next time you see one on display I'm sure you'll find him worth a long look, for he is a beautiful and rare member of the cat family. Perhaps you'll even hear him "sawing wood."

$5\frac{3}{4}''$

F

$5\frac{1}{4}''$

H

16. TIGER
Felis tigris

The Asians have a saying: "As uncertain as a tiger," and it is most descriptive of the unpredictable reactions of this greatest of the wild cats. Usually a tiger will slink away if he spots a human in the forest or jungle, but at another time, apparently unmindful of the presence of man, he will hurl himself at a goat or cow being led on a short rope by a man, or two men, down a jungle trail. This same great cat may pass up a favorite meal just because he can hear people working or talking in a field perhaps half a mile away.

Generally tigers, no matter where they are found, seem to detest the taste and smell of human beings, and even shy away from his buildings, which is just fine with me. On the other hand, this unpredictable cat may suddenly turn to humans for his main delicacy. One tiger was known to kill 80 men in a single year, another killed 213 humans during his lifetime, and

108

in some districts of Bengal, over 300 humans have been killed by "stripes" in a single year.

Although outwardly quite different from a lion, the two appear to be almost identical when skinned, with the lion a bit smaller. The largest of the tigers come from south central Siberia and western China, where they reach a length of over twelve feet (some say thirteen feet) and reach a weight of over 550 pounds. One was reported at 650 pounds and thirteen feet in length. They stand three feet high at the shoulder and have a four-foot tail.

The tigers of India and Bengal are a bit smaller, reaching nine or ten feet in length and a weight of perhaps 450 pounds. The tiger females are somewhat smaller than the males, Bengal females weigh about 350 pounds. In Sumatra the tigers are smaller yet, weighing less than half of what a big Bengal tiger weighs.

The biggest cats are from Siberia, where they grow exceptionally long, thick, coats. Perhaps nature is trying especially hard to help them survive, for in north China more albino and semi-albino tigers are born than in any other part of the world. The semi-albinos have faint brown stripes, but are generally almost white.

The Bengal tiger wears the same coat as that of the other family branches, but the stripes are narrower. All have the same yellow-orange background color, but those from the colder climes of north China seem to have the brightest coats.

The stripes running down the sides of tigers never match on both sides, but the markings on the face and head usually do. The tail is long and banded with black, ending in a black tip. The upper lips, chin, and under parts are creamy white, and a black-banded white patch appears over each eye; the eyes themselves are rimmed with white. The long, stiff whiskers are dark at the roots, and some I have seen are almost seven inches long. These grow from dark spots on the lips and enable the big cat to feel his way through small openings with safety. Long side whiskers of orange-yellow and black and white rim the face, and the ears are rounded and set quite well back on the head. The legs are banded with dark stripes, especially the outer side of the hind legs. The insides of the legs may be white occasionally, marked with dark bars.

Sometimes a jet-black tiger appears, even in the snow country of the Siberian tiger's range, where he stands out like a lump of coal in a sugar bowl. How such a cat ever gets close enough to grab a meal is a mystery, unless he *does* pose as a rock ledge or perhaps a pile of coal. The black stripes of the normally colored tigers continue on into the long hair of the belly, and also around into the white hair of the throat.

Tigers living in the jungles find that their coats are ideal camouflage for both hunting and their own safety, for it blends perfectly with the lights and shadows there. Only one thing keeps the tiger from being among nature's finest jungle hunting machines: he seldom ever looks above him into the trees for a possible enemy. Having never been a tree climber, he is apparently instinctively unaware that danger can come from above as well as on his own level. He looks left and right but seldom ever sees the hunter perched overhead on a branch or platform erected over his trail. This is often his undoing.

Tigers have keen hearing, a poor sense of smell, and even poorer eyesight, so they usually hunt by ear. Strangely enough, if a possible victim stands perfectly still, which is a pretty neat trick with a tiger prowling close by, the beast may miss it completely and have to hunt further on. Tigers kill by leaping upon their victims, hugging them and biting their throats, rather than by killing them with a blow from a paw or by strangulation, as do the lions and cheetahs. They eat as much as two hundred pounds of beef at one sitting, drinking great amounts of water

TIGER — *Felis tigris*

with it, and then cover the remains with brush while they rest nearby for another meal later on.

The tiger, although never a climber himself, will use tree trunks for sharpening his claws like smaller cats, and sometimes these claws scratches can be found as much as eight feet up on the trunk. He rips and tears the bark with his ten front claws to clean, toughen, and sharpen them.

Being a great hunter with a huge appetite, he requires a big and adequate supply of fresh meat. Bengal farmers and cattle raisers have lost as many as sixty thousand farm animals of all types in a single year to this big cat. In India, however, he is protected as a valuable predator to keep deer and other browsing animals under control which protects the grass for domestic animals.

"Stripes" will eat almost anything, including elephant, buffalo, domestic animals of all kinds, and even fish when other things are scarce. One of his favorite delicacies is the pangolin, or scaly anteater, which is covered with huge hard scales. He will eat one of these slow-moving nocturnal oddities at any time. One interesting side light of this hankering for a dinner of pangolin is that in China, where these pangolin scales are considered of great medicinal value, tiger dens are often raided for the scales, which frequently litter the floor.

The tigers usually hunt from dark until eight or nine the next morning if they are still hungry, and during the day lie up in their den or in some shady nook where they can see but not be easily seen themselves. The natives credit the tiger with the same fishing skill as the jaguar, that of dunking its tail in the water and then swishing it aloft with fish hanging onto the hairs. Undoubtedly they do occasionally splash fish out of the water, as do some of the bears and other cats, but as for the story about tigers using their tails as fishing lines, I'll have to vote "no."

Although tigers like to swim and love to lie in shallow pools to cool themselves when the weather is hot, they have a dislike of getting the morning dew on their sleek coats. As a result, they stick to well-worn and opened game trails in the morning, and that is when many of them are shot by hunters who know the trails. Tigers swim well and powerfully and have been known to cross even small salt-water bays or coves to get to the other side, rather than go around by land.

The young of the tiger are born at almost any time of the year in hot climates and in the warmest months where the weather is colder. The kittens or cubs number from one to six but are usually four in a litter. The cats mate every other year. The kittens stay with the parents, or at least the mother, for about two years, or until another litter displaces them. They mature at about three years and then establish their own families.

The kittens are born blind and cannot open their eyes for about two weeks. They weigh two or three pounds at birth, and the sexes are usually evenly divided in a litter. Usually only two cubs survive to mature, and it is reported that in the wild state the parents often eat unwanted cubs. In captivity tigers breed well, and many females have several cubs while in captivity. One Bengal tiger female, famous as the mother of fine litters, produced thirty-two cubs in less than twenty years at the famed Bronz Zoo in New York City. Many of her offspring are now exhibited in zoos around the world. Tigers often live to be twenty-five years or more.

Where it is possible, tigers find a rocky den in which to have their cubs, but if the mother is not in a territory with ledges and rocks, the cubs are born in secluded thickets or in beds made in the tall grass and reeds.

The voice of the tiger includes a growl, a roar for special

occasions, snarls, and an explosive "woof" when surprised or startled. He has one other noise, which he makes when hunting or when apparently disturbed over something. This is a soft sound difficult to describe, which is almost bell-like or birdlike— about the most untigerish noise an animal can make. When stalking an animal, the tiger is silent, but occasionally when a charge misses its mark and the victim escapes, he will cut loose with a roar or snarl of frustration.

Wounded tigers react differently. According to hunters the males usually roar, while their mates keep silent, making the female a far more dangerous animal to track down once it has been hit. A wounded and silent tiger hiding in head-high grass or dense jungle is a problem no sportsman enjoys facing, even when hunting from the back of an elephant.

Although most tigers are hunted from high platforms in trees, or from the backs of elephants, with the tiger being driven toward the hunter by beaters on foot, I've just come across another interesting method. I have a very old book on natural history published long before the turn of the century, which describes how tigers are captured in "Oude," a place I cannot find in an atlas, but which apparently is in India, or was there.

According to this book, once the track of a tiger has been located, the natives collect a huge pile of leaves from the prouss tree, "which are like those of the sycamore." These leaves are spread with a sort of sticky substance made from crushed berries and then scattered, sticky side up, where hunters hope the tiger will step when "returning for a nap," as they say. When he does come back, he steps upon one of the sticky leaves, and his troubles begin. The more he tries to get rid of the sticky leaf, the more he steps on them, and soon becomes covered with them and helpless, to be destroyed by the natives, or, as this ancient volume puts it, "The anxiety produced by this strange and novel predicament [being covered with the sticky leaves] soon discovers itself in dreadful howlings, which serve to call the watchful peasants, who in this state find no difficulty in shooting the mottled object of their detestation." Well, that's one way to say it.

The size of the tiger's track depends upon the branch of the clan that makes it, but even the smallest tigers leave a most impressive one. Some of the largest leave paw prints six inches long and almost as wide. The claws do not register, and the hind feet usually step in the paw prints of the front feet, which are slightly larger.

Tigers also cover their droppings, scratching up the dirt with their paws for the purpose. These are called "scrapes" and are a sure sign the big cats have been in the territory. Another sign is the dusting spot where the big cats have rolled in the dust to rid their fur of insects. This can sometimes be found in arid areas, and the cats like to roll in the fine sand and then shake themselves afterwards as a dog does after a bath, or a horse does after a good roll in the corral dust.

According to some scientists, tigers probably originated as an arctic animal, and apparently in northern Siberia, from where they spread southward in two emigrations. One went down through Manchuria and Korea to China and eventually to India, Indochina, Malaya, Sumatra, Java, and Bali. The other emigration headed for southwestern Asia, to Afghanistan and Iran, and to the Caucasus. It's a shame that some didn't come this way, for with all the romantic lore and legend surrounding the tiger it would be exciting to think that perhaps a few of them might be found in this country outside of a zoo enclosure.

According to zoo keepers, some tigers seem to fade in coloring once they have been in captivity for a while, while others seem to thrive on the regular meals and good care. I can't imagine a tiger ever fading in any way under any circumstances, and like the animal in William Blake's famous poem, "Tiger! tiger! burning bright, in the forests of the night," they shine with a special glow, as far as I'm concerned, no matter where they are.

Photograph by R. Van Nostrand, from National Audubon Society

116

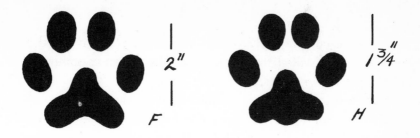

17. TIGER CAT
Felis bengalensis

The name "tiger cat" has been applied to a wide variety of small striped and spotted cats from various parts of the world, but this little chap is generally accepted as being the original and genuine article. He is also called the "leopard cat" and the "Bengal cat" as well.

The tiger cat is about the size of an ordinary house cat, perhaps a bit larger, and is a brownish yellow above and a creamy white below, as are many similar and larger jungle cats. He has a wild variety of spots and blotches of black over his upper body, head, and legs, with scattered spots on its underside and on the inside of its legs. The neck and the top of his head in particular are marked with stripes, and a white stripe outlines his eyes and the side of his nose. The lips and chin are white, and the long, sensitive whiskers sprout from rows of black dots along his upper lip.

The tail is spotted or ringed, and the flanks are covered with uniformly sized spots, which in southern China has resulted in the cat's being called the "money cat," as the spots somewhat resemble Chinese coins.

There are several phases of this little cat, each with its own local name and slight variation. His range includes: Kashmir, India, eastern Tibet, all of China, Manchuria, and Korea, and he is also found in Formosa, Borneo, and the Philippines. Almost any place where there is scrub brush or a forest in which he can hide and hunt is a home for this little spotted member of the cat family. He is also occasionally found quite close to civilization, for once he has found the delights of a chicken coop or hen yard, he stays as close as safety permits to this new-found "shopping center."

Normally he stays in the thick brush, forest, or jungle, and feeds on small mammals and birds. He hunts by night, and with his speed and agility both on the ground and in the trees can easily catch his dinner high or low, wherever he finds it. One of his favorite dinners is a roosting bird he can pounce upon in the darkness. His night sight is excellent, and his climbing skill the best. He is seldom found in a treeless, arid area.

The tiger cat is about three feet long, with a one-foot tail included. One study skin from Korea I measured was thirty-two inches long, including a nine-inch tail, and one tiny skin from a tiger cat kitten found outside the South East Gate of the city of Peking in China was thirteen inches long with a three-inch tail. The feet of this little creature measured only half an inch long, about the size of squirrel paws. Another pelt from Mount Wuchi, in the province of Shensi, China, was twenty-four inches long and had paws only three-quarters of an inch in length, so you can see they are not very big, as wild cats go. In some areas and with some closely allied species, these miniature "jaguars" may be slightly larger or smaller, but generally they are all about this size.

The kittens are born in the spring or summer, except in the very hot countries, when apparently they may appear at almost any time of the year. They number two to four in a litter and are very slow to develop compared with the sometimes astonishingly rapid growth of other young animals. For example, two nursing tiger cat kittens found in China in late May were still unusually small six months later, in December. This may have been due to unusual conditions, but as the kittens seemed to be healthy, it may be characteristic of the little chaps to take their time growing up.

The den of the mother tiger cat may be in a dense thicket or under a protecting ledge, hollow log or tree. She much prefers the hollow log or tree, where she feels safer from a possible enemy. Being a fine climber, she likes to be up off the ground for family life, or taking a quiet nap between shopping trips.

The only real enemies of the tiger cat are larger cats on the prowl, native hunters, and native trappers who know he will bring a fine price from the world's zoos. His preference for dense cover, his camouflage coat, and his nocturnal habits do much to keep his kind alive and plentiful over a great part of the globe.

The voice of this little feline is about like that of any good, rugged alley cat—a mixture of squalls and yowls in the mating season, with snarls, hisses, and spitting noises for the rest of the year. He, like all cats, is a silent stalker of his prey, so saves his breath for leisure-time vocalizing, or when he meets an enemy.

He has favorite scratching trees or posts to sharpen his tiny claws upon and keep them clean. He often returns to these favorite "whetstones" time and again if he finds one to his particular liking. He not only keeps his weapons clean and sharp but his coat and whiskers as well, grooming himself after a meal or a good sound nap. The mother grooms her kittens, washing them and teaching them how to be neat and presentable, which, like most youngsters, they probably resent wholeheartedly.

The tracks of this bright little jungle cat show by the roundness of the paw prints that he is a good climber used to a lot of arboreal hunting in the branches for his food. Cats who do most of their hunting on the ground usually have paws more elongated than rounded. The tracks measure about one or one and a half inches long, depending upon size and age of the little creature. No claws show in the tracks, and the hind feet can be smaller than the front paws.

Regardless of the particular phase in which the little tiger cat may be found, this little striped and spotted feline has made a home for himself in almost every corner of Asia and appears to be doing quite well wherever he is found. A sporty little animal, he is a colorful addition to the landscape. By any other name—"leopard cat," "Bengal cat," or "money cat"—he is just as colorful, but "tiger cat" seems to fit him to a "T"—perhaps for Tiger.